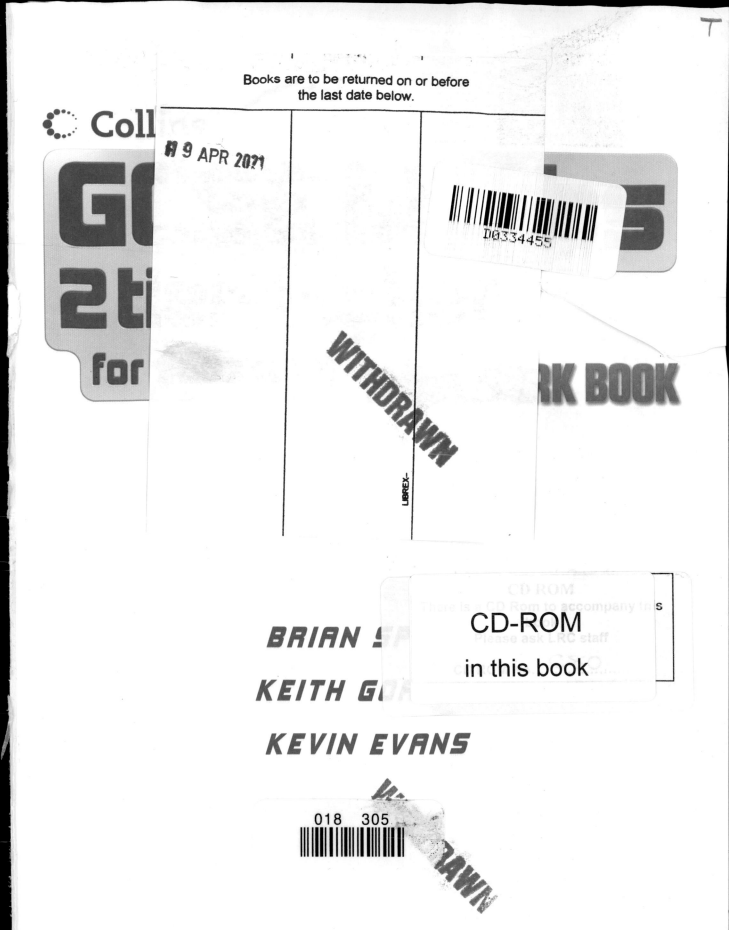

Coll...

G...
2ti...
for ...

...RK BOOK

BRIAN S...

KEITH G...

KEVIN EVANS

William Collins' dream of knowledge for all began with the publication of his first book in 1819. A self-educated mill worker, he not only enriched millions of lives, but also founded a flourishing publishing house. Today, staying true to this spirit, Collins books are packed with inspiration, innovation and practical expertise. They place you at the centre of a world of possibility and give you exactly what you need to explore it.

Collins. Do more.

Published by Collins
An imprint of HarperCollins*Publishers*
77–85 Fulham Palace Road
Hammersmith
London
W6 8JB

Browse the complete Collins catalogue at
www.collinseducation.com

10 9 8 7 6

ISBN-13 978-0-00-721566-9
ISBN-10 0-00-721566-5

British Library Cataloguing in Publication Data
A Catalogue record for this publication is available from the British Library

Acknowledgements

Publishing Manager Michael Cotter

Cover design by Andy Parker and JPD

Internal design by JPD

Page make-up by JPD

Production by Natasha Buckland

Printed and bound in Great Britain by Martins the Printers, Berwick upon Tweed

Contents

This homework book is designed to give you extra practice on the topics covered in class. Each exercise in the Collins GCSE Maths textbooks has a corresponding homework exercise of the same format in this book.

Occasionally, the homework may start with a worked example to ease you into the exercise and remind you of what you were doing in class. Included with this homework book is a CD-ROM containing versions of the Collins GCSE Maths textbook in electronic form. You may find it helpful to look at the relevant textbook page again, when doing your homework.

A few homework exercises include an "examination-type question" and they are highlighted with an asterisk * in the margin. These questions give you the opportunity to see how each topic might appear in your examinations.

We do hope you enjoy using Collins GCSE Maths, and we wish you every success in your studies!

Brian Speed, Keith Gordon, Kevin Evans

Developed by the team behind the highly popular and successful Maths Frameworking series, Collins GCSE Maths is the easiest way to achieve success in 2 tier Mathematics.

Instructions for using the CD-ROM

1. Insert the CD-ROM into your CD drive

2. The CD should run immediately

3. From the main menu, choose the textbook that you are using at school

4. Locate the Chapter you are working on, and open it.

5. Using the scroll bars to find the appropriate page you need.

If you experience any technical difficulties, contact **help@collinseducation.com** with details.

1 Number

Read the problem carefully and then do the calculation to solve the problem.

1 Wall tiles are packed in boxes of 16. Andy buys 24 packs to tile his bathroom. How many tiles does he buy altogether?

2 The organiser of a church fete requires 1000 coloured balloons. How many packets does she need to buy if there are 25 balloons in a packet?

3 A TV rental shop purchases 32 televisions at £112 each.
   a Find the total cost of the televisions.
   b Show how you could check your answer by estimation.

4 The annual subscription fee to join a fishing club is £42. The treasurer of the club has collected £1134 in fees. How many people have paid their subscription fee?

5 Mrs Woodhead saves £14 per week towards her bills. How much does she save in a year?

6 Sylvia has a part time job and is paid £18 for every day she works. Last year she worked for 148 days. How much was she paid for the year?

7 A coach firm charges £504 for 36 people to go Christmas shopping on a day trip to Calais. How much does each person pay if they share the cost equally between them?

8 A concert hall has 48 rows of seats with 32 seats in a row. What is the maximum capacity of the hall?

★**9** Allan is a market gardener and has 420 bulbs to plant. He plants them out in rows with 18 bulbs to a row. How many complete rows will there be?

★**10** A room measuring 6 metres by 8 metres is to be carpeted. The carpet costs £19 per square metre.
   a Estimate the cost of the carpet.
   b Calculate the exact cost of the carpet.

1 Evaluate each of these.
   a $7.2 \div 0.2$ **b** $32 \div 0.8$ **c** $0.36 \div 0.4$ **d** $8.1 \div 0.9$
   e $3.58 \div 0.2$ **f** $7.85 \div 0.5$ **g** $22.5 \div 0.03$ **h** $0.726 \div 0.06$

2 Evaluate each of these.
   a $39.1 \div 0.23$ **b** $5.74 \div 0.41$ **c** $0.384 \div 2.4$ **d** $71.4 \div 0.17$
   e $13 \div 0.25$ **f** $140.4 \div 0.52$ **g** $0.384 \div 1.6$ **h** $72 \div 0.45$

1 Round off each of the following numbers to 1 significant figure.

a	46 313	**b**	57 123	**c**	30 569	**d**	94 558	**e**	85 299
f	54.26	**g**	85.18	**h**	27.09	**i**	96.432	**j**	167.77
k	0.5388	**l**	0.2823	**m**	0.005 84	**n**	0.047 85	**o**	0.000 876
p	9.9	**q**	89.5	**r**	90.78	**s**	199	**t**	999.99

2 What is the least and the greatest number of people that can be found in these towns?

Hellaby   population 900 (to 1 significant figure)

Hook   population 650 (to 2 significant figures)

Hundleton   population 1050 (to 3 significant figures)

3 Round off each of the following numbers to 2 significant figures.

a	6725	**b**	35 724	**c**	68 522	**d**	41 689	**e**	27 308
f	6973	**g**	2174	**h**	958	**i**	439	**j**	327.6

4 Round off each of the following to the number of significant figures (sf) indicated.

a	46 302 (1 sf)	**b**	6177 (2 sf)	**c**	89.67 (3 sf)	**d**	216.7 (2 sf)		
e	7.78 (1 sf)	**f**	1.087 (2 sf)	**g**	729.9 (3 sf)	**h**	5821 (1 sf)		
i	66.51 (2 sf)	**j**	5.986 (1 sf)	**k**	7.552 (1 sf)	**l**	9.7454 (3 sf)		
m	25.76 (2 sf)	**n**	28.53 (1 sf)	**o**	869.89 (3 sf)	**p**	35.88 (1 sf)		
q	0.084 71 (2 sf)	**r**	0.0099 (2 sf)	**s**	0.0809 (1 sf)	**t**	0.061 97 (3 sf)		

1 Without using a calculator, write down the answer to these.

a	50×600	**b**	0.6×40	**c**	0.02×400	**d**	$(30)^2$
e	0.5×250	**f**	0.6×0.7	**g**	$30 \times 40 \times 50$	**h**	$200 \times 0.7 \times 40$

2 Without using a calculator, write down the answer to these.

a	$4000 \div 20$	**b**	$8000 \div 200$	**c**	$400 \div 0.5$	**d**	$2000 \div 0.05$
e	$1800 \div 0.12$	**f**	$600 \div 0.3$	**g**	$200 \times 30 \div 40$	**h**	$300 \times 70 \div 0.4$

1 Find approximate answers to the following sums.

a	4324×6.71	**b**	6170×7.311	**c**	72.35×3.142
d	4709×3.81	**e**	$63.1 \times 4.18 \times 8.32$	**f**	$320 \times 6.95 \times 0.98$
g	$454 \div 89.3$	**h**	$26.8 \div 2.97$	**i**	$4964 \div 7.23$
j	$316 \div 3.87$	**k**	$2489 \div 48.58$	**l**	$63.94 \div 8.302$

2 Find the approximate monthly pay of the following people whose annual salary is

a	Joy £47 200	**b**	Amy £24 200	**c**	Tom £19 135

3 Find the approximate annual pay of these brothers who earn

    a   Trevor £570 a week   **b**   Brian £2728 a month

4 A litre of creosote will cover an area of about 6.8 m². Approximately how many litre cans will I need to buy to creosote a fence with a total surface area of 43 m²?

★**5** A groundsman bought 350 kg of seed at a cost of £3.84 per kg. Find the approximate total cost of this seed.

6   A greengrocer sells a box of 250 apples for £47. Approximately how much did each apple sell for?

7   Keith runs about 15 km every day. Approximately how far does he run in
    a   a week   **b**   a month   **c**   a year?

HOMEWORK 1F

1   Round off each of the following figures to a suitable degree of accuracy.
    a   Kris is 1.6248 metres tall.
    b   It took me 17 minutes 48.78 seconds to cook the dinner.
    c   My rabbit weighs 2.867 kg.
    d   The temperature at the bottom of the ocean is 1.239 °C.
    e   There were 23 736 people at the game yesterday.

2   How many jars each holding 119 cm^3 of water can be filled from a 3 litre flask?

3   If I walk at an average speed of 62 metres per minute, how long will it take me to walk a distance of 4 km?

4   Helen earns £31 500 a year. How much does she earn in
    a   1 month   **b**   1 week   **c**   1 day?

5   Dave travelled a distance of 350 miles in 5 hours 40 minutes. What was his average speed?

6   Ten grams of gold cost £2.17. How much will one kilogram of gold cost?

HOMEWORK 1G

1   From the list of numbers below
        28   19   36   43   64   53   77   66   56   60   15   29   61   45   51

    Write down those that are
    a   multiples of 4   **b**   multiples of 5   **c**   prime numbers   **d**   factors of 2700

2   During the peak travel time at a railway station, there are trains setting off to the north every 8 minutes, there are trains to the south every 12 minutes. At 5 pm a train sets off to the north and one sets off to the south. How many more times will two trains be setting off at the same time before 6.30 pm?

3   Write down the negative square root of each of these.
    a   36   **b**   81   **c**   100   **d**   900   **e**   361
    f   169   **g**   225   **h**   1 000 000   **i**   441   **j**   1225

4   Write down the cube root of each of these.
    a   8   **b**   64   **c**   125   **d**   1000   **e**   27 000
    f   −27   **g**   −1   **h**   −216   **i**   −8000   **j**   −343

5   Write down the value of each of these.
    a   √0.36   **b**   √0.81   **c**   √1.69   **d**   √0.09   **e**   √0.01
    f   √1.44   **g**   √2.25   **h**   √1.96   **i**   √4.41   **j**   √12.25

1 Draw factor trees for the following numbers.

a 144 **b** 75 **c** 98 **d** 420 **e** 560

2 Write the factors for the following in index notation.

a 48 **b** 54 **c** 216 **d** 1000 **e** 675

1 Find the LCM of each of these pairs of numbers.

a 5 and 7 **b** 3 and 8 **c** 6 and 9 **d** 10 and 12
e 10 and 15 **f** 12 and 16 **g** 16 and 24 **h** 15 and 35

2 Find the HCF of each of these pairs of numbers.

a 21 and 49 **b** 27 and 45 **c** 15 and 25 **d** 25 and 45
e 48 and 60 **f** 72 and 108 **g** 54 and 126 **h** 99 and 132

3 Find the HCF of 55 555 and 67 750

4 Find the LCM of 144 and 162

1 Write down the answers to the following.

a -2×4 **b** -3×6 **c** -5×7 **d** -3×-4 **e** -8×-2
f $-14 \div -2$ **g** $-16 \div -4$ **h** $25 \div -5$ **i** $-16 \div -8$ **j** $-8 \div -4$
k 3×-7 **l** 6×-3 **m** 7×-4 **n** -3×-9 **o** -7×-2
p $28 \div -4$ **q** $12 \div -3$ **r** $-40 \div 8$ **s** $-15 \div -3$ **t** $50 \div -2$
u -3×-8 **v** $42 \div -6$ **w** 7×-9 **x** $-24 \div -4$ **y** -7×8

2 Write down the answers to the following.

a $-2 + 4$ **b** $-3 + 6$ **c** $-5 + 7$ **d** $-3 + -4$ **e** $-8 + -2$
f $-14 - -2$ **g** $-16 - -4$ **h** $25 - -5$ **i** $-16 - -8$ **j** $-8 - -4$
k $3 + -7$ **l** $6 + -3$ **m** $7 + -4$ **n** $-3 + -9$ **o** $-7 + -2$
p $28 - -4$ **q** $12 - -3$ **r** $-40 - 8$ **s** $-15 - -3$ **t** $50 - -2$
u $-3 + -8$ **v** $42 - -6$ **w** $7 + -9$ **x** $-24 - -4$ **y** $-7 + 8$

3 What number do you multiply -5 by to get the following?

a 25 **b** -30 **c** 50 **d** -100 **e** 75

1 Work out each of these. Remember: first work out the bracket.

a $-3 \times (-2 + 6)$ **b** $8 \div (-3 + 2)$ **c** $(6 - 8) \times -3$ **d** $-4 \times (-6 - 3)$
e $-5 \times (-6 \div 2)$ **f** $(-5 + 3) \times -3$ **g** $(6 - 9) \times -4$ **h** $(2 - 5) \times (5 - 2)$

2 Work out each of these.

a $-5 \times -4 + 3$ **b** $-8 \div 8 - 3$ **c** $16 \div -4 + 3$ **d** $2 \times -5 + 6$
e $-3 \times 4 - 5$ **f** $-1 + 4^2 - 5$ **g** $5 - 3^2 + 2$ **h** $-1 + 2 \times -3$

3 Copy each of these and then put in a bracket to make each one true.

    a $4 \times -3 + 2 = -4$ **b** $-6 \div -3 + 2 = 4$ **c** $-6 \div -3 + 2 = 6$

4 $a = -3, b = 5, c = -4$

    Work out the values of the following.

    a $(a + b)^2$ **b** $-(a + c)^2$ **c** $(a + b)c$ **d** $a^2 + b^2 + c^2$

2   Fractions and percentages

HOMEWORK 2A

1 Write the first quantity as a fraction of the second.

    a 5p, 20p   **b** 4 kg, 12 kg   **c** 6 hours, 12 hours

    d 14 days, 30 days   **e** 6 days, 2 weeks   **f** 20 minutes, 2 hours

2 David scored 18 goals out of his team's season total of 48 goals. What fraction of all the goals did David score?

3 James works for 32 weeks a year. What fraction of the year does he work for?

HOMEWORK 2B

1 Evaluate the following.

    a $\frac{1}{2} + \frac{1}{5}$ **b** $\frac{1}{2} + \frac{1}{3}$ **c** $\frac{1}{3} + \frac{1}{10}$ **d** $\frac{3}{8} + \frac{1}{3}$

    e $\frac{3}{4} + \frac{1}{5}$ **f** $\frac{1}{3} + \frac{2}{5}$ **g** $\frac{3}{5} + \frac{3}{8}$ **h** $\frac{1}{2} + \frac{2}{5}$

2 Evaluate the following.

    a $\frac{1}{2} + \frac{1}{4}$ **b** $\frac{1}{3} + \frac{1}{6}$ **c** $\frac{3}{5} + \frac{1}{10}$ **d** $\frac{5}{8} + \frac{1}{4}$

3 Evaluate the following.

    a $\frac{7}{8} - \frac{3}{4}$ **b** $\frac{4}{5} - \frac{1}{2}$ **c** $\frac{2}{3} - \frac{1}{5}$ **d** $\frac{3}{4} - \frac{2}{5}$

4 Evaluate the following.

    a $\frac{5}{8} + \frac{3}{4}$ **b** $\frac{1}{2} + \frac{3}{5}$ **c** $\frac{5}{6} + \frac{1}{4}$ **d** $\frac{2}{3} + \frac{3}{4}$

5 At a football club half of the players are English, a quarter are Scottish and one sixth are Italian. The rest are Irish. What fraction of players at the club are Irish?

6 On a firm's coach trip, half the people were employees, two fifths were partners of the employees. The rest were children. What fraction of the people were children?

7 Five eighths of the 35 000 crowd were male. How many females were in the crowd?

8 What is four fifths of sixty-five added to five sixths of fifty-four?

1 Evaluate the following, leaving your answer in its simplest form.

a $\frac{1}{2} \times \frac{2}{3}$ **b** $\frac{3}{4} \times \frac{2}{5}$ **c** $\frac{3}{5} \times \frac{1}{2}$ **d** $\frac{3}{7} \times \frac{2}{3}$ **e** $\frac{2}{3} \times \frac{5}{6}$

f $\frac{1}{3} \times \frac{3}{5}$ **g** $\frac{2}{3} \times \frac{7}{10}$ **h** $\frac{3}{8} \times \frac{2}{5}$ **i** $\frac{4}{9} \times \frac{3}{8}$ **j** $\frac{4}{5} \times \frac{7}{16}$

2 Evaluate the following, leaving your answer as a mixed number where possible.

a $1\frac{1}{3} \times 2\frac{1}{4}$ **b** $1\frac{3}{4} \times 1\frac{1}{3}$ **c** $2\frac{1}{2} \times \frac{4}{5}$ **d** $1\frac{2}{3} \times 1\frac{3}{10}$

e $3\frac{1}{4} \times 1\frac{3}{5}$ **f** $2\frac{2}{3} \times 1\frac{3}{4}$ **g** $3\frac{1}{2} \times 1\frac{1}{6}$ **h** $7\frac{1}{2} \times 1\frac{3}{5}$

3 Kris walked three quarters of the way along Carterknowle Road which is 3 km long. How far did Kris walk?

4 Jean ate one fifth of a cake, Les ate a half of what was left. Nick ate the rest. What fraction of the cake did Nick eat?

5 Billie made a cast that weighed five and three quarter kilograms. Four fifths of this weight is water. What is the weight of the water in Billie's cast?

6 Which is the smaller, $\frac{3}{4}$ of $5\frac{1}{3}$ or $\frac{2}{3}$ of $4\frac{2}{5}$?

★7 I bought twenty-four bottles of lemonade, all containing $2\frac{3}{4}$ litres of lemonade. What is the total amount of lemonade I bought?

1 Evaluate the following, leaving your answer as a mixed number where possible.

a $\frac{1}{5} \div \frac{1}{3}$ **b** $\frac{3}{5} \div \frac{3}{8}$ **c** $\frac{4}{5} \div \frac{2}{3}$ **d** $\frac{4}{7} \div \frac{8}{9}$

e $4 \div 1\frac{1}{2}$ **f** $5 \div 3\frac{2}{3}$ **g** $8 \div 1\frac{3}{4}$ **h** $6 \div 1\frac{1}{4}$

i $5\frac{1}{2} \div 1\frac{1}{3}$ **j** $7\frac{1}{2} \div 2\frac{2}{3}$ **k** $1\frac{1}{2} \div 1\frac{1}{5}$ **l** $3\frac{1}{2} \div 3\frac{3}{4}$

2 A pet shop has thirty-six kilograms of hamster food. Tom, who owns the shop, wants to pack this into bags, each containing three quarters of a kilogram. How many bags can he make in this way?

★3 Bob is putting a fence down the side of his garden, it is to be 20 metres long. The fence comes in sections; each one is one and one third of a metre long. How many sections will Bob need to put the fence all the way down the one side of his garden?

4 An African bullfrog can jump a distance of $1\frac{1}{4}$ metres in one hop. How many hops would it take an African bullfrog to hop a distance of 100 metres?

5 Evaluate the following, leaving your answer as a mixed number wherever possible.

a $\frac{4}{5} \times \frac{1}{2} \times \frac{3}{8}$ **b** $\frac{3}{4} \times \frac{7}{10} \times \frac{5}{6}$ **c** $\frac{2}{3} \times \frac{5}{6} \times \frac{9}{10}$

d $1\frac{1}{4} \times \frac{2}{3} \div \frac{5}{6}$ **e** $\frac{5}{8} \times 1\frac{1}{3} \div 1\frac{1}{10}$ **f** $2\frac{1}{2} \times 1\frac{1}{3} \div 3\frac{1}{3}$

1 Increase each of the following by the given amount.

a £80 by 5%   **b** 14 kg by 6%   **c** £42 by 3%

2 Increase each of the following by the given amount.

a 340 g by 10%   **b** 64 m by 5%   **c** £41 by 20%

3 Keith, who was on a salary of £34 200, was given a pay rise of 4%. What was his new salary?

4 In 1991 the population of Dripfield was 14 200. By 2001 that had increased by 8%. What was the population of Dripfield in 2001?

5 In 1993 the number of bikes on the roads of Doncaster was about 840. Since then it has increased by 8%. Approximately how many bikes are on the roads of Doncaster now?

6 At a nightclub there are always about 30% more girls than boys. If at one disco there were 40 boys, how many girls were there?

★**7** A house was priced at £42 000 in January 1999. In January 2000, it was 4% more expensive. In January 2001, it was 5% more expensive than the price in 2000. What was the price of the house in January 2001?

HOMEWORK 2F

1 Decrease each of the following by the given amount.
   a £8 by 4%   **b** 17 kg by 6%   **d** 240 m by 2%

2 Decrease each of the following by the given amount.
   a 360 g by 10%   **b** 440 m by 15%   **c** 360 cm by 25%

3 A van valued at £8400 last year is now worth 12% less. What is its value now?

4 A firm employed 80 workers. But it had to streamline its workers and lose 20% of the workers. How many workers does the firm have now?

5 On the first day of a new term, a school expects to have an attendance rate of 99%. If the school population is 700 pupils, how many pupils will the school expect to be absent on the first day of the new term?

★**6** Most weighing scales in the home have an error of about 10% from the true reading. When my weighing scales say 500 grams, what is the
   a lowest weight it could represent   **b** largest weight it could represent?

7 By putting cavity wall insulation into your home, you could use 20% less fuel. A family using an average of 850 units of electricity a year, put cavity wall insulation into their home. How much electricity would they expect to use now?

8 Prove that a 10% increase followed by a 10% decrease is equivalent to a 1% increase overall.

HOMEWORK 2G

1 Express the following as percentages.
   a £4 of £16   **b** £3 of £50   **c** 25 kg of 500 kg
   d 12 hours of 1 day   **e** 15 minutes of 1 hour   **f** 13 m of 20 m

2 Find the percentage profit on the following.

Item	Retail price (selling price)	Wholesale price (price the shop paid)
a DVD	£210	£150
b Widescreen TV	£840	£500

3 There were four left-handed pupils in a class of 25. What percentage were left-handed?

4 James came home from school one day with his end-of-year test results. Change each of James' results to a percentage.

Maths   63 out of 75   English   56 out of 80
Science   75 out of 120   French   27 out of 60

★5 Kris had an annual salary of £32 000 in 2000, which was increased to £33 600 in 2001. What percentage increase does this represent?

6 During the wet year of 1993, it rained in London on 80 days of the year. What percentage of days were wet? Give your answer to two significant figures.

HOMEWORK 2H

1 A small plant increases its height by 10% each day in the second week of its growth. At the end of the first week, the plant was 5 cm high.
What is its weight after a further

a 1 day   **b** 2 days   **c** 4 days   **d** 1 week?

2 The headmaster of a new school offered his staff an annual pay increase of 5% for every year they stayed with the school.

a Mr Speed started teaching at the school on a salary of £28 000. What salary will he be on after 3 years if he stays at the school?

b Miss Tuck started teaching at the school on a salary of £14 500. How many years will it be until she is earning a salary of over £20 000?

3 Billy put a gift of £250 into a special savings account that offered him 8% compound interest if he promised to keep the money in for at least 2 years. How much was in this account after

a 2 years   **b** 3 years   **c** 5 years?

4 The penguin population of a small island was only 1500 in 1998, but it steadily increased by about 15% each year. Calculate the population in

a 1999   **b** 2000   **c** 2002

★5 A sycamore tree is 40 cm tall; it grows at a rate of 8% per year. A conifer is 20 cm tall. It grows at a rate of 15% per year. How many years does it take before the conifer is taller than the sycamore?

HOMEWORK 2I

1 Find what 100% represents when
a 20% represents 160 g   **b** 25% represents 24 m   **c** 5% represents 42 cm

2 Find what 100% represents when
a 40% represents 28 kg   **b** 30% represents £54   **c** 15% represents 6 hours

3 VAT is a government tax added to goods and services. With VAT at 17.5%, what is the pre-VAT price of the following priced goods?
Jumper   £14.10   Socks   £1.88   Trousers   £23.50

4 Paula spends £9 each week on CDs. This is 60% of her weekly income. How much is Paula's weekly income?

5 Alan's weekly pay is increased by 4% to £187.20. What was Alan's pay before the increase?

6 Kev sold his bike for £60, making a profit of 20% on the price he paid for it. How much did Kev pay for the bike?

★7 Gran used 240 g of mixed fruit and nut in a cake. This represented 30% of the weight of the cake. How much did the cake weigh?

8 99 Rock music CDs represents just 18% of my entire CD collection. How many CDs have I?

3 Ratios and proportion

HOMEWORK 3A

Example 1 Simplify 5 : 20.

$$5 : 20 = 1 : 4 \quad \text{(Divide both sides of the ratio by 5)}$$

Example 2 Simplify 20p : £2.

(Change to a common unit) 20p : 200p = 1:10

Example 3 A garden is divided into lawn and shrubs in the ratio 3 : 2.

The lawn covers $\frac{3}{5}$ of the garden and the shrubs cover $\frac{2}{5}$ of the garden.

1 Express each of the following ratios in their simplest form.
a	3 : 9	**b**	5 : 25	**c**	4 : 24	**d**	10 : 30	**e**	6 : 9
f	12 : 20	**g**	25 : 40	**h**	30 : 4	**i**	14 : 35	**j**	125 : 50

2 Express each of the following ratios of quantities in their simplest form. (Remember to change to a common unit where necessary.)
a	£2 to £8	**b**	£12 to £16	**c**	25 g to 200 g
d	6 miles : 15 miles	**e**	20 cm : 50 cm	**f**	80p : £1.50
g	1 kg : 300 g	**h**	40 seconds : 2 minutes	**i**	9 hours : 1 day
j	4 mm : 2 cm				

3 £20 is shared out between Bob and Kathryn in the ratio 1 : 3.
a What fraction of the £20 does Bob receive?
b What fraction of the £20 does Kathryn receive?

4 In a class of students, the ratio of boys to girls is 2 : 3.
a What fraction of the class is boys?
b What fraction of the class is girls?

5 Pewter is an alloy containing lead and tin in the ratio 1 : 9.
a What fraction of pewter is lead?
b What fraction of pewter is tin?

Example   Divide £40 between Peter and Hitan in the ratio 2 : 3.

Changing the ratio to fractions gives
Peter's share = $\frac{2}{5}$ and Hitan's share = $\frac{3}{5}$
So, Peter receives $\frac{2}{5} \times £40 = £16$ and Hitan receives $\frac{3}{5} \times £40 = £24$

1   Divide each of the following amounts in the given ratios.
   a   £10 in the ratio 1 : 4   **b**   £12 in the ratio 1 : 2
   c   £40 in the ratio 1 : 3   **d**   60 g in the ratio 1 : 5
   e   10 hours in the ratio 1 : 9   **f**   25 kg in the ratio 2 : 3
   g   30 days the ratio 3 : 2   **h**   70 m in the ratio 3 : 4
   i   £5 in the ratio 3 : 7   **j**   1 day in the ratio 5 : 3

2   The ratio of female to male members of a Sports Centre is 3 : 1. The total number of members of the Centre is 400.
   a   How many members are female?   **b**   How many members are male?

3   A 20 metre length of cloth is cut into two pieces in the ratio 1 : 9. How long is each piece?

4   James collects beer mats and the ratio of British mats to foreign mats is 5 : 2. He has 1400 beer mats in his collection. How many foreign beer mats does he have?

5   Patrick and Jane share out a box of sweets in the ratio of their ages. Patrick is 9 years old and Jane is 11 years old. If there are 100 sweets in the box, how many does Patrick get?

★**6**   For her birthday Reena is given £30. She decides to spend four times as much as she saves. How much does she save?

7   Mrs Megson calculates that her quarterly electricity and gas bills are in the ratio 5 : 6. The total she pays for both bills is £66. How much is each bill?

8   You can simplify a ratio by changing it into the form 1 : n. For example, 5 : 7 can be rewritten as 5 : 7 = 1 : 1.4 by dividing each side of the ratio by 5. Rewrite each of the following ratios in the form 1 : n.
   a   2 : 3   **b**   2 : 5   **c**   4 : 5   **d**   5 : 8   **e**   10 : 21

Example   Two business partners, John and Ben, divided their total profit in the ratio 3 : 5. John received £2100. How much did Ben get?

John's £2100 was $\frac{3}{8}$ of the total profit.
So, $\frac{1}{8}$ of the total profit = £2100 ÷ 3 = £700.
Therefore, Ben's share, which was $\frac{5}{8}$, amounted to £700 × 5 = £3500.

1   Peter and Margaret's ages are in the ratio 4 : 5. If Peter is 16 years old, how old is Margaret?

2   Cans of lemonade and packets of crisps were bought for the school disco in the ratio 3 : 2. The organiser bought 120 cans of lemonade. How many packets of crisps did she buy?

3 In his restaurant, Manuel is making 'Sangria', a drink made from red wine and iced soda water, mixed in the ratio 2 : 3. Manuel uses 10 litres of red wine.

    a How many litres of soda water does he use?

    b How many litres of Sangria does he make?

4 Cupro-nickel coins are minted by mixing copper and nickel in the ratio 4 : 1.

    a How much copper is needed to mix with 20 kg of nickel?

    b How much nickel is needed to mix with 20 kg of copper?

5 The ratio of male to female spectators at a school inter-form football match is 2 : 1. If 60 boys watched the game, how many spectators were there in total?

★6 Marmalade is made from sugar and oranges in the ratio 3 : 5. A jar of 'Savilles' marmalade contains 120 g of sugar.

    a How many grams of oranges are in the jar?

    b How many grams of marmalade are in the jar?

★7 Each year Abbey School holds a sponsored walk for charity. The money raised is shared between a local charity and a national charity in the ratio 1 : 2. Last year the school gave £2000 to the local charity.

    a How much did the school give to the national charity?

    b How much did the school raise in total?

HOMEWORK 3D

The relationship between speed, time and distance can be expressed in three ways:

$$\text{Distance} = \text{Speed} \times \text{Time} \qquad \text{Speed} = \frac{\text{Distance}}{\text{Time}} \qquad \text{Time} = \frac{\text{Distance}}{\text{Speed}}$$

Example   Sean is going to drive from Newcastle upon Tyne to Nottingham, a distance of 190 miles. He estimates that he will drive at an average speed of 50 mph. How long will it take him?

Sean's time = $\frac{190}{50}$ = 3.8 hours

Change the 0.8 hours to minutes by multiplying by 60, to give 48 minutes. So, the time for Sean's journey will be 3 hours 48 minutes.

Remember   When you calculate a time and get a decimal answer, do not mistake the decimal part for minutes. You must either

- leave the time as a decimal number and give the unit as hours, or
- change the decimal part to minutes by multiplying it by 60 (1 hour = 60 minutes) and give the answer in hours and minutes.

1 A cyclist travels a distance of 60 miles in 4 hours. What was her average speed?

2 How far along a motorway will you travel if you drive at an average speed of 60 mph for 3 hours?

3 Mr Baylis drives on a business trip from Manchester to London in $4\frac{1}{2}$ hours. The distance he travels is 207 miles. What is his average speed?

4 The distance from Leeds to Birmingham is 125 miles. The train I catch travels at an average speed of 50 mph. If I catch the 11.30 am train in Leeds, at what time would I expect to be in Birmingham?

5 Copy and complete the following table.

	Distance travelled	Time taken	Average speed
a	240 miles	8 hours	
b	150 km	3 hours	
c		4 hours	5 mph
d		$2\frac{1}{2}$ hours	20 km/h
e	1300 miles		400 mph
f	90 km		25 km/h

★**6** A coach travels at an average speed of 60 km/h for 2 hours on a motorway and then slows down in a town centre to do the last 30 minutes of a journey at an average speed of 20 km/h.
  a What is the total distance of this journey?
  b What is the average speed of the coach over the whole journey?

★**7** Hilary cycles to work each day. She cycles the first 5 miles at an average speed of 15 mph and then cycles the last mile in 10 minutes.
  a How long does it take her to get to work?
  b What is her average speed for the whole journey?

★**8** Martha drives home from work in 1 hour 15 minutes. She drives home at an average speed of 36 mph.
  a Change 1 hour 15 minutes to decimal time in hours.
  b How far is it from Martha's work to her home?

9 Change the following speeds to metres per minute.
  a 24 km/h   **b** 18 km/h   **c** 45 km/h   **d** 120 km/h   **e** 750 km/h

10 Change the following speeds to kilometres per hour.
  a 35 m/s   **b** 15 m/s   **c** 600 m/s   **d** 40 m/s   **e** 8000 m/s

HOMEWORK 3E

Example   If eight pens cost £2.64, what is the cost of five pens?

First find the cost of one pen. This is £2.64 ÷ 8 = £0.33
The cost of five pens is £0.33 × 5 = £1.65

1 If four video tapes cost £3.20, what would ten video tapes cost?

2 Five oranges cost 90p. Find the cost of twelve oranges.

3 Dylan earns £18.60 in 3 hours. How much will he earn in 8 hours?

4 Barbara bought 12 postcards for 3 euros when she was on holiday in Tenerife.
  a How many euros would she have paid if she had only bought 9 postcards?
  b How many postcards could she have bought with a 5 euro note?

5 Five 'Day-Rover' bus tickets cost £8.50.
  a What is the cost of 16 tickets?
  b How many tickets can be bought for £20?

6 A car uses 8 litres of petrol on a trip of 72 miles.
  a How much would be used on a trip of 54 miles?

b How far would the car go on a full tank of 45 litres?

7 It takes a photocopier 18 seconds to produce 12 copies. How long will it take to produce 32 copies?

★**8** Val has a recipe for making 12 flapjacks.
    100 g margarine
    4 tablespoons golden syrup
    80 g granulated sugar
    200 g rolled oats
a What is the recipe for
    i 6 flapjacks   **ii** 24 flapjacks   **iii** 30 flapjacks
b What is the maximum number of flapjackts she can make if she has 1 kg of each ingredient?

HOMEWORK 3F

Example   There are two different-sized packets of Whitto soap powder at a supermarket.

The medium size contains 800 g and costs £1.60 and the large size contains 2.5 kg and costs £4.75. Which is the better buy?

Find the weight per unit cost for both packets.
    Medium: 800 ÷ 160 = 5 g per penny
    Large: 2500 ÷ 475 = 5.26 g per penny

From these we see that there is more weight per penny with the large size, which means that the large size is the better buy.

1 Compare the following pairs of product and state which is the better buy and why.
a Tomato ketchup: a medium bottle which is 200 g for 55p or a large bottle which is 350 g for 87p.
b Milk chocolate: a 125 g bar at 77p or a 200 g bar at 92p.
c Coffee: a 750 g tin at £11.95 or a 500 g tin at £7.85.
d Honey: a large jar which is 900 g for £2.35 or a small jar which is 225 g for 65p.

2 Boxes of 'Wetherels' teabags are sold in three different sizes.

Small — 80 teabags £1.44   Medium — 120 teabags £2.10   Large — 200 teabags £3.25

Which size of teabags gives the best value for money?

3 Bottles of 'Cola' are sold in different sizes. Copy and complete the table.

Size of bottle	Price	Cost per litre
$\frac{1}{2}$ litre	36p	
$1\frac{1}{2}$ litre	99p	
2 litres	£1.40	
3 litres	£1.95	

Which bottle gives the best value for money?

★**4** The following 'special offers' were being promoted at a supermarket.

Only £1.99 each

Cornflakes
750 g
£1.99

Buy 3 for the price of 2

Cornflakes
500 g
£1.69

Which offer is the better value for money? Explain why.

1 Find the density of a piece of wood weighing 135 g and having a volume of 150 cm^3.

2 Calculate the density of a metal if 40 cm^3 of it weighs 2500 g.

3 Calculate the weight of a piece of plastic, 25 cm^3 in volume, if its density is 1.2 g/cm^3.

4 Calculate the volume of a piece of wood which weighs 350 g and has a density of 0.7 g/cm^3.

5 Find the weight of a statue, 540 cm^3 in volume, if the density of marble is 2.5 g/cm^3.

6 Calculate the volume of a liquid weighing 1 kg and having a density of 1.1 g/cm^3.

7 Find the density of the material of a stone which weighs 63 g and has a volume of 12 cm^3.

★**8** It is estimated that a huge rock balanced on the ceiling of a cave has a volume of 120 m^3. The density of the rock is 8.3 g/cm^3. What is the estimated weight of the rock?

9 A 1 kg bag of flour has a volume of about 900 cm^3. What is the density of flour in g/cm^3?

4 **Shape**

1 Find the circumference of each of the following circles, round off your answers to 1 dp.
   a Diameter 3 cm   **b** Radius 5 cm   **c** Radius 8 m
   d Diameter 14 cm   **e** Diameter 6.4 cm   **f** Radius 3.5 cm

2 John runs twice round a circular track which has a radius of 50 m. How far has he run? Give your answers in terms of π.

3 A rolling pin has a diameter of 5 cm.
   a What is the circumference of the rolling pin?
   b How many revolutions does it make when rolling a length of 30 cm?

4 What is the total perimeter of a semicircle of diameter 7 cm? Give your answer to 1 dp.

5 What is the total perimeter of a semicircle of radius 6 cm? Give your answer in terms of π.

6 How many complete revolutions will a bicycle wheel, radius 28 cm, make in a journey of 3 km?

★7 A circle has a circumference of 12 cm. What is its diameter?

8 Calculate the area of each of these circles, giving your answers to 1 decimal place, except for **a** and **d**, where your answer should be in terms of π.
  a Radius 4 cm   **b** Diameter 14 cm   **c** Radius 9 cm
  d Diameter 2 m   **e** Radius 21 cm   **f** Diameter 0.9 cm

9 A garden has a circular lawn of diameter 20 m. There is a path 1 m wide all the way round the circumference. What is the area of this path?

10 Calculate the area of a semi-circle with a diameter of 15 cm. Give your answer to 1 dp.

11 A circle has an area of 50 m². What is its radius?

★12 I have a circle with a circumference of 25 cm. What is the area of this circle?
Give your answer to 1 decimal place.

13 Jane walked around a circular lawn. She counted 153 paces to walk round it. Each of her paces was about 42 cm. What is the area of the lawn?

HOMEWORK 4B

1 Calculate the perimeter and the area of each of these trapeziums.

a

b

2 Calculate the area of each of these shapes.

a

b

3 Calculate the area of the shaded part in each of these diagrams.

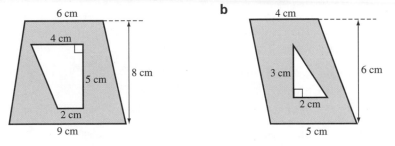

a

b

4 Which of the following shapes has the largest area?

a

3 cm

2.5 cm

5 cm

b

8 cm

2.4 cm

5 What percentage of this shape has been shaded?

7 cm

5 cm

6 cm

3 cm

7 cm

10 cm

HOMEWORK 4C

1 For these sectors, calculate the arc length and the sector area.

a

50°

10 cm

b

90°

7 cm

2 Calculate the arc length and the area of a sector whose arc subtends a right angle in a circle of diameter 10 cm. Give your answer in terms of π.

3 Calculate the total perimeter of each of these shapes.

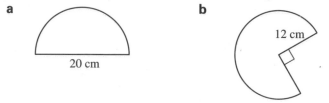

a

20 cm

b

12 cm

4 Calculate the area of each of these shapes.

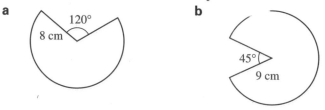

a

120°

8 cm

b

45°

9 cm

★5   There is an infrared sensor in a security system. The
      sensor can detect movement inside a sector of a circle. The
      radius of the circle is 16 m. The sector is 120°. Calculate the
      area of the sector.

HOMEWORK 4D

1   Find the density of a piece of wood weighing 189 g and having a volume of 210 cm^3.

2   Calculate the density of a metal if 56 cm^3 of it weighs 3500 g.

3   Calculate the weight of a piece of plastic, 24 cm^3 in volume, if its density is 1.25 g/cm^3.

4   Calculate the volume of a piece of wood which weighs 450 g and has a density of
    0.7 g/cm^3.

5   Find the weight of a statue, 500 cm^3 in volume, if the density of marble is 2.7 g/cm^3.

6   Calculate the volume of a liquid weighing 1.6 kg and having a density of 1.76 g/cm^3.

7   Find the density of the material of a stone which weighs 84 g and has a volume of
    16 cm^3.

★8   It is estimated that a huge rock balanced on the roof of a cave has a volume of 150 m^3.
      The density of the rock is 6.64 g/cm^3. What is the estimated weight of the rock?

9   A 1 kg bag of flour has a volume of about 1350 cm^3. What is the density of flour in g/cm^3?

HOMEWORK 4E

1   For each prism shown, calculate the area of the cross-section and the volume.

    a   b

2   Which of these solids is
    a   the heaviest   b   the lightest?

1   Find **i** the volume and **ii** the curved surface area of a cylinder with base radius 5 cm and height 4 cm. Give your answer in terms of π.

2   Find **i** the volume and **ii** the curved surface area of a cylinder with base radius 8 cm and height 17 cm. Give your answer to a suitable degree of accuracy.

3   Find **i** the volume and **ii** the total surface area of each of these cylinders.

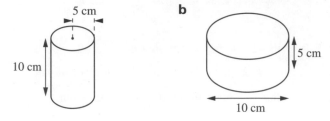

a   5 cm

10 cm

b   5 cm

10 cm

4   What is the radius of a cylinder, height 6 cm, with a volume of 24π cm^3?

5   What is the radius of a cylinder, height 10 cm, with a curved surface area of 360π cm^2?

6   What is the height of a cylinder, diameter 12 cm, with a volume of 108π cm^3?

7   A cylinder of height 20 cm has a curved surface area of 200 cm^2. Calculate the volume of this cylinder.

8   Calculate the curved surface area of a cylinder which has a height of 18 cm and a volume of 390 cm^3.

★9   A cylinder has the same height and radius. The total surface area is 100π. Calculate the volume. Give your answer in terms of π.

1   Calculate the volume of each of these pyramids, both with rectangular bases.

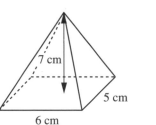

a   7 cm

5 cm

6 cm

b   13 cm

16 cm

30 cm

2   Calculate the volume of a pyramid having a square base of side 10 cm and a vertical height of 18 cm.

3   Calculate the volume of this shape.

6 m

3 m

5 m

6 m

4 Calculate the height h of a rectangular-based
pyramid with a length of 14 cm, a width of 10 cm and a volume of 140 cm³.

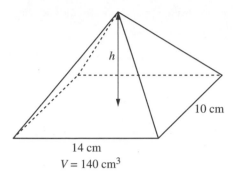

14 cm

10 cm

$V = 140$ cm³

★**5** The pyramid in the diagram has its top half cut off
as shown. The shape which is left is called a frustum.
Calculate the volume of the frustum.

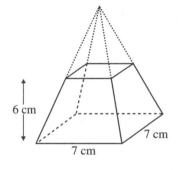

6 cm

7 cm

7 cm

HOMEWORK 4H

1 For each cone, calculate **i** its volume and **ii** its total surface area. (The units are cm.)

a

34

30

32

b

6

8

10

2 Find the total surface area of a cone whose base radius is 4 cm and slant height is 6 cm.
Give your answer in terms of π.

3 Find the volume of a cone whose base radius is 6 cm and vertical height is 8 cm. Give
your answer in terms of π.

4 In order to make a cone, a sector of angle 60° is cut
from a circle whose radius is 12 cm.

60°

12 cm

    a Calculate the circumference of the base of the cone.
    b Calculate the radius of the base of the cone.
    c State the length of the slant height of the cone.
    d Calculate the curved surface area of the cone.
    e Calculate the vertical height of the cone.
    f Calculate the volume of the cone.

5 A container in the shape of a cone, base radius 10 cm and vertical height 19 cm, is full of
water. The water is poured into an empty cylinder of radius 15 cm. How high is the water
in the cylinder?

★6 The diagram shows a paper cone. The diameter of the base is 4.8 cm and the slant height is 4 cm. The cone is cut along the line AV and opened out flat, as shown below.

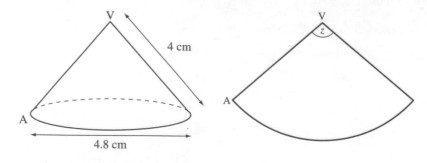

Calculate the size of angle z.

1 Calculate the volume of each of these spheres. Give your answers in terms of π.
   a Radius 3 cm   **b** Diameter 30 cm

2 Calculate the surface area of each of these spheres. Give your answers in terms of π.
   a Radius 4 cm   **b** Diameter 10 cm

3 Calculate the volume and the surface area of a sphere with a diameter of 30 cm. Give your answers to a suitable degree of accuracy

4 Calculate, correct to 1 decimal place, the radius of a sphere
   a whose surface area is 200 cm^2 **b** whose volume is 200 cm^3.

5 The volume of a sphere is 50 m^3. Find its diameter.

6 What is the volume of a sphere whose surface area is 400 cm^2?

★7 A spinning top which consists of a cone of base radius 6 cm, slant height 10 cm and a hemisphere of radius 6 cm, is illustrated on the right. Give your answers in terms of π.
   a Calculate the volume of the spinning top.
   b Calculate the total surface area of the spinning top.

5   Algebra 1

1 Find the value of $4x + 3$ when   **i** $x = 3$ **ii** $x = 6$ **iii** $x = 11$

2 Find the value of $3k - 1$ when   **i** $k = 2$ **ii** $k = 5$ **iii** $k = 10$

3 Find the value of $4 + t$ when   **i** $t = 5$ **ii** $t = 8$ **iii** $t = 15$

4 Evaluate $14 - 3f$ when   **i** $f = 4$ **ii** $f = 6$ **iii** $f = 10$

5 Evaluate $\dfrac{4d-7}{2}$ when   **i** $d = 2$ **ii** $d = 5$ **iii** $d = 15$

6 Find the value of $5x + 2$ when   **i** $x = -2$ **ii** $x = -1$ **iii** $x = 21.5$

7 Evaluate $4w - 3$ when   **i** $w = -2$ **ii** $w = -3$ **iii** $w = 2.5$

8 Evaluate $10 - x$ when   **i** $x = -3$ **ii** $x = -6$ **iii** $x = 4.6$

9 Find the value of $5t - 1$ when   **i** $t = 2.4$ **ii** $t = -2.6$ **iii** $t = 0.05$

10 Evaluate $11 - 3t$ when   **i** $t = 2.5$ **ii** $t = -2.8$ **iii** $t = 0.99$

11 Where $H = a^2 + c^2$, find H when   **a** $a = 3$ and $c = 4$ **b** $a = 5$ and $c = 12$

12 Where $K = m^2 - n^2$, find K when   **a** $m = 5$ and $n = 3$ **b** $m = -5$ and $n = -2$

13 Where $P = 100 - n^2$, find P when   **a** $n = 7$ **b** $n = 8$ **c** $n = 9$

14 Where $D = 5x - y$, find D when   **a** $x = 4$ and $y = 3$ **b** $x = 5$ and $y = -3$

15 Where $T = y(2x + 3y)$, find T when   **a** $x = 8$ and $y = 12$ **b** $x = 5$ and $y = 7$

16 Where $m = w(t^2 + w^2)$, find m when   **a** $t = 5$ and $w = 3$ **b** $t = 8$ and $w = 7$

HOMEWORK 5B

Expand these expressions.

1 $3(4 + m)$ **2** $6(3 + p)$ **3** $4(4 - y)$ **4** $3(6 + 7k)$

5 $4(3 - 5f)$ **6** $2(4 - 23w)$ **7** $7(g + h)$ **8** $4(2k + 4m)$

9 $6(2d - n)$ **10** $t(t + 5)$ **11** $m(m + 4)$ **12** $k(k - 2)$

13 $g(4g + 1)$ **14** $y(3y - 21)$ **15** $p(7 - 8p)$ **16** $2m(m + 5)$

17 $3t(t - 2)$ **18** $3k(5 - k)$ **19** $2g(4g + 3)$ **20** $4h(2h - 3)$

21 $2t(6 - 5t)$ **22** $4d(3d + 5e)$ **23** $3y(4y + 5k)$ **24** $6m^2(3m - p)$

25 $y(y^2 + 7)$ **26** $h(h^3 + 9)$ **27** $k(k^2 - 4)$ **28** $3t(t^2 + 3)$

29 $5h(h^3 - 2)$ **30** $4g(g^3 - 3)$ **31** $5m(2m^2 + m)$ **32** $2d(4d^2 - d^3)$

33 $4w(3w^2 + t)$ **34** $3a(5a^2 - b)$ **35** $2p(7p^3 - 8m)$ **36** $m^2(3 + 5m)$

37 $t^3(t + 3t)$ **38** $g^2(4t - 3g^2)$ **39** $2t^2(7t + m)$ **40** $3h^2(4h + 5g)$

HOMEWORK 5C

1 Simplify these expressions.
   a $5t + 4t$ **b** $4m + 3m$ **c** $6y + y$ **d** $2d + 3d + 5d$
   e $7e - 5e$ **f** $6g - 3g$ **g** $3p - p$ **h** $5t - t$
   i $t^2 + 4t^2$ **j** $5y^2 - 2y^2$ **k** $4ab + 3ab$ **l** $5a^2d - 4a^2d$

2 Expand and simplify.
   a $3(2 + t) + 4(3 + t)$ **b** $6(2 + 3k) + 2(5 + 3k)$ **c** $5(2 + 4m) + 3(1 + 4m)$
   d $3(4 + y) + 5(1 + 2y)$ **e** $5(2 + 3f) + 3(6 - f)$ **f** $7(2 + 5g) + 2(3 - g)$

3 Expand and simplify.
   a $4(3 + 2h) - 2(5 + 3h)$ **b** $5(3g + 4) - 3(2g + 5)$ **c** $3(4y + 5) - 2(3y + 2)$
   d $3(5t + 2) - 2(4t + 5)$ **e** $5(5k + 2) - 2(4k - 3)$ **f** $4(4e + 3) - 2(5e - 4)$

4 Expand and simplify.
   a $m(5 + p) + p(2 + m)$ **b** $k(4 + h) + h(5 + 2k)$ **c** $t(1 + 2n) + n(3 + 5t)$
   d $p(5q + 1) + q(3p + 5)$ **e** $2h(3 + 4j) + 3j(h + 4)$ **f** $3y(4t + 5) + 2t(1 + 4y)$

5 Expand and simplify.
   a $t(2t + 5) + 2t(4 + t)$ **b** $3y(4 + 3y) + y(6y - 5)$ **c** $5w(3w + 2) + 4w(3 - w)$
   d $4p(2p + 3) - 3p(2 - 3p)$ **e** $4m(m - 1) + 3m(4 - m)$ **f** $5d(3 - d) + d(2d - 1)$

6 Expand and simplify.
   a $5a(3b + 2a) + a(2a^2 + 3c)$ **b** $4y(3w + y^2) + y(3y - 4t)$

HOMEWORK 5D

Factorise the following expressions.

1 $9m + 12t$ **2** $9t + 6p$ **3** $4m + 12k$ **4** $4r + 6t$

5 $2mn + 3m$ **6** $4g^2 + 3g$ **7** $4w - 8t$ **8** $10p - 6k$

9 $12h - 10k$ **10** $4mp + 2mk$ **11** $4bc + 6bk$ **12** $8ab + 4ac$

13 $3y^2 + 4y$ **14** $5t^2 - 3t$ **15** $3d^2 - 2d$ **16** $6m^2 - 3mp$

17 $3p^2 + 9pt$ **18** $8pt + 12mp$ **19** $8ab - 6bc$ **20** $4a^2 - 8ab$

21 $8mt - 6pt$ **22** $20at^2 + 12at$ **23** $4b^2c - 10bc$ **24** $4abc + 6bed$

25 $6a^2 + 4a + 10$ **26** $12ab + 6bc + 9bd$ **27** $6t^2 + 3t + at$

28 $96mt^2 - 3mt + 69m^2t$ **29** $6ab^2 + 2ab - 4a^2b$ **30** $5pt^2 + 15pt + 5p^2t$

Factorise the following expressions where possible. List those which cannot factorise.

31 $5m - 6t$ **32** $3m + 2mp$ **33** $t^2 - 5t$ **34** $6pt + 5ab$

35 $8m^2 - 6mp$ **36** $a^2 + c$ **37** $3a^2 - 7ab$ **38** $4ab + 5cd$

39 $7ab - 4b^2c$ **40** $3p^2 - 4t^2$ **41** $6m^2t + 9t^2m$ **42** $5mt + 3pn$

HOMEWORK 5E

Solve the following equations.

1 $\dfrac{g}{3} + 2 = 8$ **2** $\dfrac{m}{4} - 5 = 2$ **3** $\dfrac{f}{6} + 3 = 12$ **4** $\dfrac{h}{8} - 3 = 5$

5 $\dfrac{2h}{3} + 3 = 7$ **6** $\dfrac{5t}{4} - 2 = 6$ **7** $\dfrac{4d}{5} + 3 = 18$ **8** $\dfrac{3x}{4} - 1 = 8$

9 $\dfrac{x + 5}{3} = 2$ **10** $\dfrac{t + 12}{2} = 5$ **11** $\dfrac{w - 3}{5} = 3$ **12** $\dfrac{y - 9}{2} = 3$

13 $\dfrac{2x - 1}{3} = 5$ **14** $\dfrac{5t + 9}{2} = 3$ **15** $\dfrac{4m + 2}{5} = 5$ **16** $\dfrac{8p - 7}{5} = 2$

7 $\dfrac{5x + 19}{4} = 4$ **18** $\dfrac{17 + 2t}{9} = 1$ **19** $\dfrac{23 + 4x}{3} = 4$ **20** $\dfrac{8 - 2x}{11} = 1$

HOMEWORK 5F

Solve the following equations. Give your answers as fractions or decimals as appropriate.

1 $3(x + 6) = 15$ **2** $6(x - 5) = 30$ **3** $4(t + 3) = 20$

4 $5(4x + 3) = 45$	**5** $3(5y - 7) = 15$	**6** $4(5x + 2) = 70$
7 $3(4t - 1) = 78$	**8** $3(4t + 5) = 51$	**9** $4(6x + 5) = 10$
10 $5(4y - 1) = 47$	**11** $5(2k + 3) = 36$	**12** $5(3x + 8) = 30$
13 $3(5y - 7) = 21$	**14** $3(6t - 5) = 57$	**15** $8(2x - 7) = 60$
16 $8(3x - 4) = 12$	**17** $4(x + 7) = 7$	**18** $3(x - 5) = -24$
19 $5(t + 3) = 12$	**20** $4(3x - 13) = 7$	**21** $5(4t + 3) = 17$
22 $2(5x - 3) = -31$	**23** $4(6y - 7) = -5$	**24** $3(2x + 7) = 9$

HOMEWORK 5G ⊗

Solve each of the following equations.

1 $3x + 4 = x + 6$	**2** $4y + 3 = 2y + 5$	**3** $5a - 2 = 2a + 4$
4 $6t + 5 = 2t + 25$	**5** $8p - 3 = 3p + 12$	**6** $5k + 4 = 2k + 13$
7 $2(d + 4) = d + 15$	**8** $4(x - 3) = 3(x + 3)$	**9** $2(3y + 2) = 5(2y - 4)$

10 $3(2b - 1) + 25 = 4(3b + 1)$ **11** $3(4c + 1) - 17 = 2(3c + 2) - 3c$

HOMEWORK 5H ⊗

Set up an equation to represent each situation described below. Then solve the equation. Do not forget to check each answer.

1 A girl is Y years old. Her father is 23 years older than she is. The sum of their ages is 37. How old is the girl?

2 A boy is X years old. His sister is twice as old as he is. The sum of their ages is 24. How old is the boy?

3 The diagram shows a rectangle. Find x if the perimeter is 24 cm.

(x + 4) cm

3 cm

4 Find the length of each side of the pentagon, if it has a perimeter of 32 cm.

x x

$x - 1$ $x - 1$

$x + 4$

5 On a bookshelf there are $2b$ crime novels, $3b - 2$ science fiction novels and $b + 7$ romance novels. Find how many of each type of book there is, if there are 65 books altogether.

★**6** Maureen thought of a number. She multiplied it by 4 and then added 6 to get an answer of 26. What number did she start with?

★**7** Declan also thought of a number. He took 4 from the number and then multiplied by 3 to get an answer of 24. What number did he start with?

★8 Sandeep's money box contains 50p coins, £1 coins and £2 coins.
In the box there are twice as many £1 coins as 50p coins and 4 more £2 coins than 50p coins. There are 44 coins in the box.
a Find how many of each coin there are in the box.
b How much money does Sandeep have in her money box?

HOMEWORK 5I

1 Find two consecutive whole numbers between which the solution to each of the following equations lies.
a $x^3 + x = 7$ b $x^3 + x = 55$ c $x^3 + x = 102$ d $x^3 + x = 89$

2 Find a solution to each of the following equations to 1 decimal place.
a $x^3 - x = 30$ b $x^3 - x = 95$ c $x^3 - x = 150$ d $x^3 - x = 333$

3 Show that $x^3 + x = 45$ has a solution between $x = 3$ and $x = 4$, and find the solution to 1 decimal place.

4 Show that $x^3 - 2x = 95$ has a solution between $x = 4$ and $x = 5$, and find the solution to 1 decimal place.

5 A rectangle has an area of 200 cm². Its length is 8 cm longer than its width. Find, correct to 1 decimal place, the dimensions of the rectangle.

6 A gardener wants his rectangular lawn to be 15 m longer than the width, and the area of the lawn to be 800 m². What are the dimensions he should make his lawn? (Give your solution to 1 decimal place.)

7 A triangle has a vertical height 2 cm longer than its base length. Its area is 20 cm². What are the dimensions of the triangle? (Give your solution to 1 decimal place.)

8 A rectangular picture has a height 3 cm shorter than its length. Its area is 120 cm². What are the dimensions of the picture? (Give your solution to 1 decimal place.)

HOMEWORK 5J

Solve the following pairs of simultaneous equations.

1 $5x + y = 17$ 2 $3x + 2y = 17$ 3 $3x - y = 7$ 4 $5x - 4y = 27$
   $3x + y = 11$ $5x + 2y = 27$ $5x + y = 17$ $2x - 4y = 12$

★5 Two numbers x and y have a sum of 16 and a difference of 9.
a Set up a pair of simultaneous equations connecting x and y.
b Solve your equations for x and y.

HOMEWORK 5K

Solve the following pairs of simultaneous equations.

1 $3x + 2y = 12$ 2 $4x + 3y = 37$ 3 $2x + 3y = 19$ 4 $5x - 2y = 14$
   $4x - y = 5$ $2x + y = 17$ $6x + 2y = 22$ $3x - y = 9$

★5 Four cups of tea and three biscuits cost £3.35.
Three cups of tea and one biscuit cost £2.20
Let x be the cost of a cup of tea and y be the cost of a biscuit.

a Set up a pair of simultaneous equations connecting x and y.

b Solve your equations for x and y and find the cost of five cups of tea and four biscuits.

HOMEWORK 5L

Solve the following simultaneous equations.

1 $6x + 5y = 23$
  $5x + 3y = 18$

2 $3x - 4y = 13$
  $2x + 3y = 20$

3 $8x - 2y = 14$
  $6x + 4y = 27$

4 $5x + 2y = 33$
  $4x + 5y = 23$

★**5** It costs two adults and three children £28.50 to go to the cinema.
It costs three adults and two children £31.50 to go to the Cinema.
Let the price of an adult ticket be £x and the price of a child's ticket be £y.

a Set up a pair of simultaneous equations connecting x and y.

b Solve your equations for x and y.

HOMEWORK 5M

Read each situation carefully, then make a pair of simultaneous equations in order to solve the problem.

1 A book and a CD cost £14.00 together. The CD costs £7 more than the book. How much does each cost?

2 Ten second-class and six first-class stamps cost £4.24. Eight second-class and ten first-class stamps cost £4.90. How much do I pay for three second-class and four first-class stamps?

3 Six cans of Coke and five chocolate bars cost £4.37. Three cans of Coke and two chocolate bars cost £2.00. How much would two cans of Coke and a chocolate bar cost?

4 Three bags of sugar and four bags of rice weigh 12 kg. Five bags of sugar and two bags of rice weigh 13 kg. What would two bags of sugar and five bags of rice weigh?

5 Two cakes and three bags of peanuts contain 63 grams of fat. One cake and four bags of peanuts contain 64 grams of fat. How many grams of fat are there in each item?

★**6** Wath School buys basic scientific calculators and graphical calculators to sell to students.
An order for 30 basic scientific calculators and 25 graphical calculators came to a total of £1240. Another order for 25 basic sscientific calculators and 10 graphical calculators came to a total of £551.25.
Using £x to represent the cost of basic scientific calculators and £y to represent the cost of graphical calculators, set up and solve a pair of simultaneous equations to find the cost of the next order which will be for 35 basic scientific calculators and 15 graphical calculators.

HOMEWORK 5N

1 $y = mx + c$ **i** Make c the subject. **ii** Express x in terms of y, m and c.

2 $v = u - 10t$ **i** Make u the subject. **ii** Express t in terms of v and u.

3 $T = 2x + 3y$ **i** Express x in terms of T and y. **ii** Make y the subject.

4 $p = q^2$ Make q the subject.

5 $p = q^2 - 3$ Make q the subject.

6 $a = b^2 + c$ Make b the subject.

★**7** A rocket is fired vertically upwards with an initial velocity of u metres per second. After t seconds the rocket's velocity, v metres per second, is given by the formula $v = u + gt$, where g is a constant.

   a Calculate v when $u = 120$, $g = -9.8$ and $t = 6$.

   b Rearrange the formula to express t in terms of v, u, and g.

   c Calculate t when $u = 100$, $g = -9.8$ and $v = 17.8$.

6   Pythagoras and trigonometry

HOMEWORK 6A

In each of the following triangles, find the hypotenuse, rounding off to a suitable degree of accuracy.

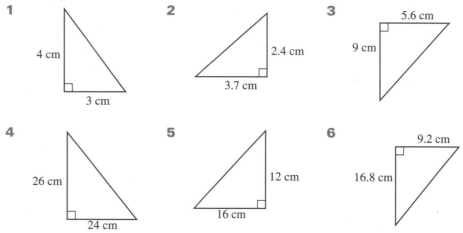

1

4 cm

3 cm

2

2.4 cm

3.7 cm

3

5.6 cm

9 cm

4

26 cm

24 cm

5

12 cm

16 cm

6

9.2 cm

16.8 cm

★**7** This diagram is not drawn to scale. It shows the cross-section of a swimming pool 50 m long. It is 3.5 m deep at the deep end. The deepest part of the pool is 10 m long.

   a Calculate the length of the sloping bottom of the pool AB.

   b The pool is 20 m wide. What is its volume?

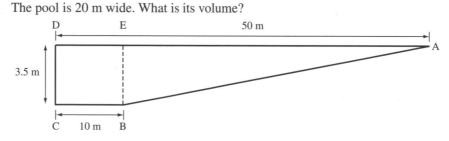

D   E   50 m

3.5 m

A

C 10 m B

1   In each of the following triangles, find the length of x to a suitable degree of accuracy.

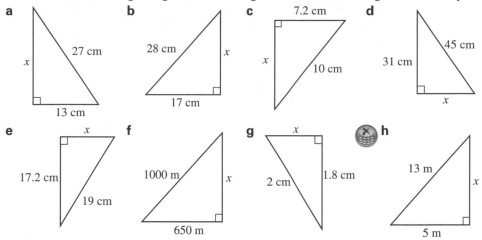

a

27 cm

x

13 cm

b

28 cm

x

17 cm

c   7.2 cm

x

10 cm

d

45 cm

31 cm

x

e x

17.2 cm

19 cm

f

1000 m

x

650 m

g x

2 cm

1.8 cm

h

13 m

x

5 m

2   In each of the following triangles, find the length of x to a suitable degree of accuracy.

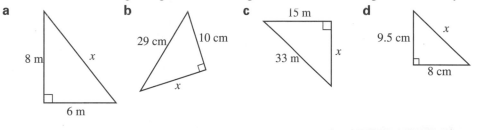

a

8 m x

6 m

b

29 cm   10 cm

x

c   15 m

33 m x

d

9.5 cm x

8 cm

★3   The diagram shows the end view of the framework for a sports arena stand. Calculate the length AB.

7 m

16 m   14 m

A   B

1   A ladder, 15 metres long, leans against a wall. The ladder reaches 12 metres up the wall. How far away from the base of the wall is the foot of the ladder.

15 m

12 m

2   A rectangle is 3 metres long and 1.2 m wide. How long is the diagonal?

3 m

1.2 m

3 How long is the diagonal of a square with a side of 10 metres?

4 A ship going from a port to a lighthouse steams 8 km east and 6 km north. How far is the lighthouse from the port?

5 At the moment, three towns, A, B and C, are joined by two roads, as in the diagram. The council wants to make a road which runs directly from A to C. How much distance will the new road save?

6 An 8 metre ladder is put up against a wall.
   a How far up the wall will it reach when the foot of the ladder is 1 m away from the wall?
   b When it reaches 7 m up the wall, how far is the foot of the ladder away from the wall?

7 How long is the line that joins the two points A(1, 3) and B(2, 2)?

8 A rectangle is 4 cm long. The length of its diagonal is 5 cm. What is the area of the rectangle?

9 Is the triangle with sides 11 cm, 6 cm and 6 cm a right-angled triangle?

10 How long is the line that joins the two points A(−3, −7), and B(4, 6)?

★**11** The diagram shows a voyage from A to position B. The boat sails due east from A for 27 km to position C. The boat then changes course and sails for 30 km to position B. On a map, the distance between A and C is 10.8 cm.
   a Work out the scale of the map.
   b Calculate the distance, in km, of B from A.

Not to scale

HOMEWORK 6D

1 Calculate the area of these isosceles triangles.

2 Calculate the area of an isosceles triangle whose sides are 10 cm, 10 cm and 8 cm.

3 Calculate the area of an equilateral triangle of side 10 cm.

4 **a** Calculate the area of an equilateral triangle of side 20 cm.

    b Explain why the answer to **4a** is not twice that of Question **3**.

5 An isosceles triangle has sides of 6 cm and 8 cm.

    a Sketch the two isosceles triangles that fit this data.

    b Which of the two triangles has the greater area?

★6 The diagram shows an isosceles triangle of base 10 mm and side 12 mm. Calculate the area of the triangle.

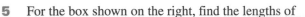

HOMEWORK 6E

1 A box measures 6 cm by 8 cm by 10 cm.

    a Calculate the lengths of

       i AC   **ii** BG   **iii** BE

    b Calculate the diagonal distance BH.

2 A garage is 5 m long, 5 m wide and 2 m high. Can a 7 m long pole be stored in it?

3 Spike, a spider, is at the corner S of the wedge shown in the diagram. Fred, a fly, is at the corner F of the same wedge.

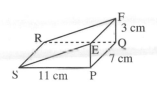

    a Calculate the two distances Spike would have to travel to get to Fred if she used the edges of the wedge.

    b Calculate the distance Spike would have to travel across the face of the wedge to get directly to Fred.

4 A corridor is 5 m wide and turns through a right angle, as in the diagram. What is the longest pole that can be carried along the corridor horizontally? If the corridor is 3 m high, what is the longest pole that can be carried along in any direction?

5 For the box shown on the right, find the lengths of

    a DG

    b HA

    c DB

    d AG

6 The diagram shows a square-based pyramid with base length 7 cm and sloping edges 12 cm. M is the mid-point of the side AB, X is the mid-point of the base, and E is directly above X.
  a Calculate the length of the diagonal AC.
  b Calculate EX, the height of the pyramid.
  c Using triangle ABE, calculate the length EM.

★**7** **a** Is the triangle with sides 9, 40, 41 cm a right-angled triangle?

  b Find the length of the diagonal AB of the cuboid 9 cm by 9 cm by 40 cm.

HOMEWORK 6F

1 Find these values, rounding off your answers to 3 sf.
  a sin 52°   **b** sin 46°   **c** sin 76.3°   **d** sin 90°

2 Find these values, rounding off your answers to 3 sf.
  a cos 52°   **b** cos 46°   **c** cos 76.3°   **d** cos 90°

3 **a** Calculate $(\sin 52°)^2 + (\cos 52°)^2$ **b** Calculate $(\sin 46°)^2 + (\cos 46°)^2$
  c Calculate $(\sin 76.3°)^2 + (\cos 76.3°)^2$ **d** Calculate $(\sin 90°)^2 + (\cos 90°)^2$
  e What do you notice about your answers?

4 Use your calculator to work out the value of
  a tan 52°   **b** tan 46°   **c** tan 76.3°   **d** tan 0°

5 Use your calculator to work out the value of
  a sin 52° ÷ cos 52°   **b** sin 46° ÷ cos 46°   **c** sin 76.3° ÷ cos 76.3°
  d sin 0° ÷ cos 0°
  e What connects your answers with the answers to Question **4**?

6 Use your calculator to work out the value of
  a 6 sin 55°   **b** 7 cos 45°   **c** 13 sin 67°   **d** 20 tan 38°

7 Use your calculator to work out the value of

  a $\dfrac{6}{\sin 55°}$ **b** $\dfrac{7}{\cos 45°}$ **c** $\dfrac{13}{\sin 67°}$ **d** $\dfrac{20}{\tan 38°}$

8 Using the following triangle, calculate sin, cos, and tan for the angle marked x. Leave your answers as fractions.

★**9** You are given that $\sin x = \dfrac{5}{\sqrt{34}}$. Work out the value of tan x.

Use your calculator to find the answers to the following. Give your answers to 1 dp.

1 What angles have sines of
   a   0.4   **b**   0.707   **c**   0.879   **d**   0.666666666666666…

2 What angles have cosines of
   a   0.4   **b**   0.707   **c**   0.879   **d**   0.333333333333333…

3 What angles have tangents of
   a   0.4   **b**   1.24   **c**   0.875   **d**   2.625

4 What angles have sines of
   a $3 \div 8$ **b** $1 \div 3$ **c** $3 \div 10$ **d** $5 \div 8$

5 What angles have cosines of
   a $3 \div 8$ **b** $1 \div 3$ **c** $3 \div 10$ **d** $5 \div 8$

6 What angles have tangents of
   a $3 \div 8$ **b** $3 \div 2$ **c** $5 \div 7$ **d** $19 \div 5$

7 You are given that $\sin 54° = 0.809$ to 3 dp. What angle has a cosine of 0.809?

1 Find the value marked x in each of these diagrams.

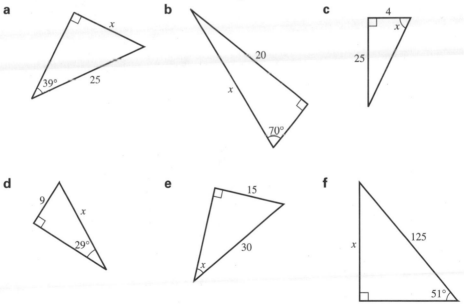

2 Angle θ has a sine of $\frac{7}{20}$. Calculate the missing lengths in these triangles.

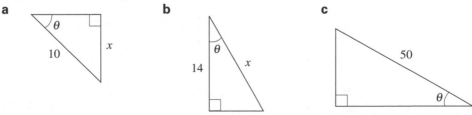

★3 Caxton is due north of Ashville and due west of
Peaton. A pilot flies directly from Ashville to Peaton,
a distance of 15 km, on a bearing of 050°.

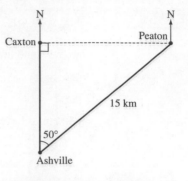

  a i   Calculate the direct distance from Caxton to
         Peaton.
     ii Find the bearing of Ashville from Peaton.

HOMEWORK 6I

1 Find the value marked x in each of these triangles.

a   b   c

d   e   f

2 Angle θ has a cosine of $\frac{7}{15}$. Calculate the missing lengths in these triangles.

a

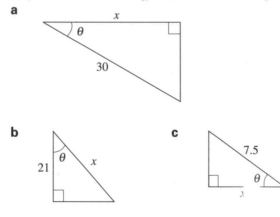

b   c

★3 The diagram shows the positions of three
telephone masts A, B and C.
Mast C is 6 kilometres due east of Mast B.
Mast A is due north of Mast B, and 9 kilometres
from Mast C.

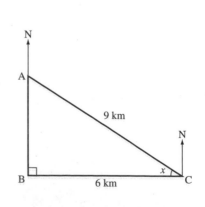

  a Calculate the distance of A from B. Give your
     answer in kilometres, correct to 3 sf.
  b Calculate the size of the angle marked x. Give
     your angle correct to 1 dp.

1 Find the value marked x in each of these triangles.

a

x
42°
17

b

x
69°
12

c

x
89
120

d

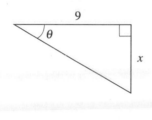

x
15
27°

e

15
27
x

f

x
76°
120

2 Angle θ has a tangent of $\frac{2}{3}$. Calculate the missing lengths in these triangles.

a

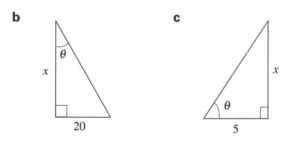

9
θ
x

b

θ
x
20

c

x
θ
5

★**3** The sensor for a security light is fixed to a house wall 2.25 m above the ground. It can detect movement on the ground up to 15 m away from the house. B is the furthest point where the sensor, A, can detect movement. Calculate the size of angle x.

A
x
2.25 m
15 m
B

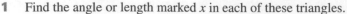

1 Find the angle or length marked *x* in each of these triangles.

a
```
    7
   x  ⌐
        |
        | 15
```

b
```
        x
  10
      ⌐  42°
```

c
```
       32°
           x
  130
      ⌐
```

d
```
      40
  18      x
        ⌐
```

e
```
  46  82°
   ⌐
      x
```

f
```
          55
  64     x
```

g
```
       x
  90     60
       ⌐
```

h
```
    ⌐  200
  x
  41°
```

i
```
       x
   ⌐     46
   85°
```

★2 The diagram shows a right-angled triangle, ABC.
Angle C = 90° and AB = 10 cm.
Given that cos B = 0.8, sin B = 0.6 and tan B = 0.75, calculate the length of AC.

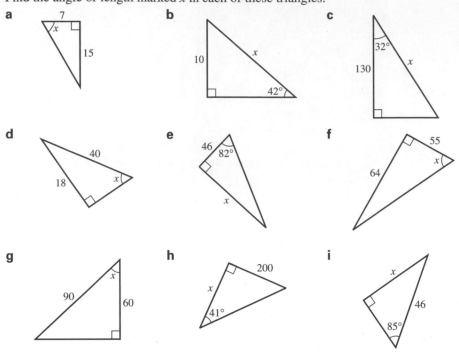

3 A lift at the seaside takes people from sea level to the top of a cliff, as shown. From sea level to the top of the cliff, the lift travels 23 m and rises a height of 21 m.

a Calculate the distance AC. Give your answer to an appropriate degree of accuracy.

b Calculate angle BCA.

1 A ladder 8 m long rests against a wall. The foot of the ladder is 2.7 m from the base of the wall. What angle does the ladder make with the ground?

2 The ladder in Question **1** has a 'safe angle' with the ground of between 70° and 80°. What are the safe limits for the distance of the foot of the ladder from the wall?

3 Angela walks 60 m from the base of a block of flats and then measures the angle from the ground to the top of the flats to be 42° as shown in the diagram. How high is the block of flats?

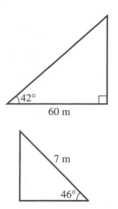

60 m

4 A slide is at an angle of 46° to the horizontal. The slide is 7 metres long. How high is the top of the slide above the ground?

7 m

46°

5 Use trigonometry to calculate the angle that the diagonal makes with the long side of a rectangle 9 cm by 5 cm.

★6 The diagram shows the end view of a building. BCD is a right-angled triangle. Angle BCD = 90°. BC = 5 m and BD = 9.5 m.
  a Calculate angle CBD.
  CH is perpendicular to AE.
  AB = ED = 3.5.
  b Calculate CH, the height of the building.

Not to scale

5 m

9.5 m

3.5 m

3.5 m

9.5 m

HOMEWORK 6M

1 Eric sees an aircraft in the sky. The aircraft is at a horizontal distance of 15 km from Eric. The angle of elevation is 42°. How high is the aircraft?

2 A man standing 100 m from the base of a block of flats looks at the top of it and notices that the angle of elevation of the top is 49°. How high are the flats?

3 A man stands 15 metres from a tree. The angle of elevation of the top of the tree from his eye is 25°. If his eye is 1.5 metres above the ground, how high is the tree?

4 A bird, sat on the very top of the tree in Question **3**, sees a worm just by the foot of the man. What is the angle of depression from the bird's eye to the worm?

5 I walk 200 metres away from a chimney that is 120 metres high. What is the angle of elevation from my eye to the top of the chimney? (Ignore the height of eye above ground.)

6 If you are now told that the height of the eye in Question **5** was 1.8 metres above ground, how much different is the angle of elevation?

★7 A boat B is moored 50 m from the foot of a vertical cliff. The angle of depression of the boat from the top of the cliff is 52°.
  a Calculate the height of the cliff.
  b The boat is released from its mooring and it drifts 350 m further away from the cliff. Calculate the angle of elevation of the top of the cliff from the boat.

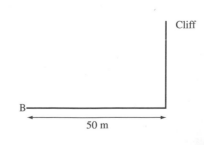

Cliff

B

50 m

1 **a** A ship sails for 85 km on a bearing of 067°. How far east has it travelled?
b How far north has the ship sailed?

2 Rotherham is 11 miles south of Barnsley and 2 miles west of Barnsley. What is the bearing of
a Barnsley from Rotherham **b** Rotherham from Barnsley?

3 A plane sets off from airport A and flies due east for 100 km, then turns to fly due south for 80 km before landing at an airport B. What is the bearing of airport B from airport A?

4 Mountain A is due east of a walker. Mountain B is due south of the walker. The guidebook says that mountain A is 5 km from mountain B, on a bearing of 038°. How far is the walker from mountain B?

5 The diagram shows the relative distances and bearings of three ships A, B and C.
a How far north of A is B?
(Distance *x* on diagram.)
b How far north of B is C?
(Distance *y* on diagram.)
c How far west of A is C?
(Distance *z* on diagram.)
d What is the bearing of A from C?
(Angle *w* on diagram.)

★**6** An aeroplane is flying from Leeds (L) to London Heathrow (H). It flies 150 miles on a bearing 136° to point A. It then turns through 90° and flies the final 80 miles to H.
a **i** Show clearly why the angle marked *x* is equal to 46°.
ii Give the bearing of H from A.
b Use Pythagoras' theorem to calculate the distance LH.
c **i** Calculate the size of the angle marked *y*.
ii Work out the bearing of L from H.

In Questions 1 and 2, find the side or angle marked *x*.

1

x

62°

9 cm

2

16 cm

x

30 cm

3 This diagram shows a roof truss. How wide is the roof?

4 Calculate the area of each of these triangles.

a

8 cm, 55°

b

65°, 16 cm

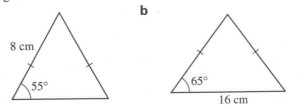

★**5** An isosceles triangle has two sides of 12 cm and an angle of 62°. Calculate both possible areas.

7 Geometry

HOMEWORK 7A

1 For each of these shapes, calculate the value of the lettered angles.

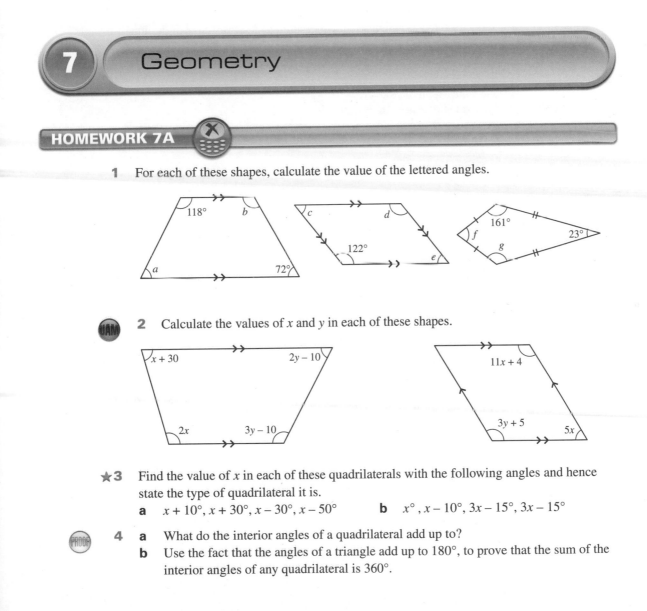

118°, b, a, 72°

c, d, 122°, e

161°, f, g, 23°

2 Calculate the values of x and y in each of these shapes.

x + 30, 2y − 10, 2x, 3y − 10

11x + 4, 3y + 5, 5x

★**3** Find the value of x in each of these quadrilaterals with the following angles and hence state the type of quadrilateral it is.

    a $x + 10°, x + 30°, x − 30°, x − 50°$ **b** $x°, x − 10°, 3x − 15°, 3x − 15°$

4 a What do the interior angles of a quadrilateral add up to?

    b Use the fact that the angles of a triangle add up to 180°, to prove that the sum of the interior angles of any quadrilateral is 360°.

1 Calculate the sum of the interior angles of polygons with
    a 7 sides   **b** 11 sides   **c** 20 sides   **d** 35 sides

2 Calculate the size of the interior angle of regular polygons with
    a 15 sides   **b** 18 sides   **c** 30 sides   **d** 100 sides

3 Find the number of sides of the polygon with the interior angle sum of
    a 1440°   **b** 2520°   **c** 6120°   **d** 6840°

4 Find the number of sides of the regular polygon with an exterior angle of
    a 20°   **b** 30°   **c** 18°   **d** 4°

5 Find the number of sides of the regular polygon with an interior angle of
    a 135°   **b** 165°   **c** 170°   **d** 156°

6 What is the name of the regular polygon whose interior angle is treble its exterior angle?

★7 Anne measured all the interior angles in a polygon. She added them up to make 1325°, but she had missed out one angle. What is the
    a name of the polygon that Anne measured and   **b** size of the missing angle?

1 Find the value of x in each of these circles with centre O.

a   **b**   **c**

d   **e**   **f**

2 Find the value of x in each of these circles.

a   **b**   **c**

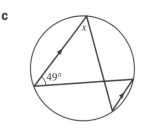

AB is a diameter

3 In the diagram, O is the centre of the circle. Find
    a ∠EDF
    b ∠DEG
    c ∠EGF

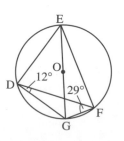

4 Find the values of *x* and *y* in each of these circles. O is the centre.

a

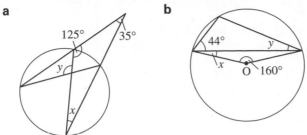

125°   35°

y

x

b

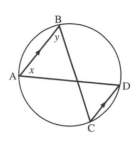

44°   *y*

x

O   160°

5 ABCD are points on a circle. AB is parallel to CD.
Prove that ∠BAD = ∠ADC

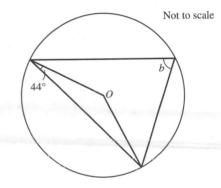

B

y

A   *x*

D

C

★**6** In each diagram, O is the centre of a circle.

a   Calculate the value of angle *a*.

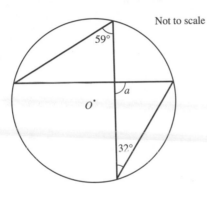

Not to scale

59°

a

O

32°

b   Calculate the value of angle *b*.

Not to scale

44°

b

O

HOMEWORK 7D

1 Find the size of the lettered angles in each of these circles.

a

80°

112°

a   *b*

b

d   *e*

f   82°

c

85°

e

d   111°

d

m

n

118°

38°

2 Find the values of x and y in each of these circles.

a

b

c

3 Find the values of x and y in each of these circles, centre O.

a

b

c

★4 ABCD are points on a circle. AB is parallel to CD.
Prove that $\angle BAC = \angle ABD$

HOMEWORK 7E

1 In each diagram, TP and TQ are tangents to a circle, centre O. Find values for r and x.

a

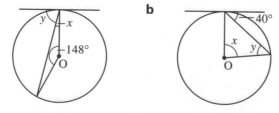

b

2 Each diagram shows a tangent to a circle, centre O. Find each value of y.

a

b

3 Each diagram shows a tangent to a circle, centre O. Find x and y in each case.

a

b

4 In each of the diagrams, TP and TQ are tangents to the circle, centre O. Find each value of x.

a

b

★**5** In the diagram, AB = AD and angle ADB = 69°.

a Work out the size of angle BED. Give reasons for each step of your working.

b Work out the size of angle BCD.

Not to scale

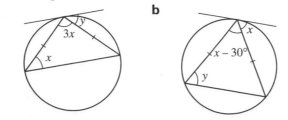

HOMEWORK 7F

1 Find the size of each lettered angle.

a

b
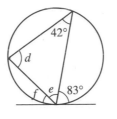

2 In each diagram, find the value of x.

a

b

3 In each diagram, find the value of x and y.

a

b

4 ATB is a tangent to the circle, centre O. Find the values of x, y and z in each case.

a

b

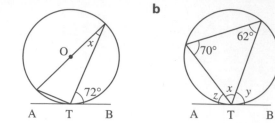

★5 O is the centre of the circle. PQT is the tangent to the circle at Q.
Work out the sizes of angles x, y and z.

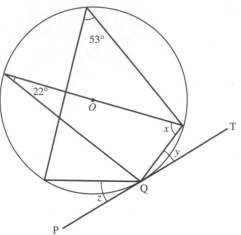

8 Transformation geometry

HOMEWORK 8A

1 State whether each pair of triangles below is congruent, giving the reasons if they are.

a **b** **c**

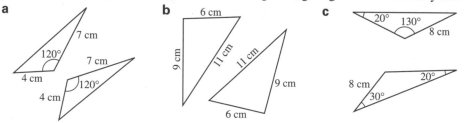

2 Draw a square ABCD. Draw in the diagonals AC and BD. Which triangles are congruent to each other?

3 Draw a kite EFGH. Draw in the diagonals EG and FH. Which triangles are congruent to each other?

4 Draw a rhombus ABCD. Draw in the diagonals AC and BD. Which triangles are congruent to each other?

5 Draw an equilateral triangle ABC. Draw the lines from each vertex to the mid-point of the opposite side. These three lines should all cross at the same point T inside the triangle. Which triangles are congruent to each other?

1 Describe with vectors these translations.

   i A to B   **ii** A to C   **iii** A to D   **iv** B to A   **v** B to C   **vi** B to D

2 **a** On a grid showing values of x and y from 0 to 10, draw the triangle with co-ordinates A(4, 4), B(5, 7) and C(6, 5).

   b Draw the image of ABC after a translation with vector $\binom{3}{2}$. Label this P.

   c Draw the image of ABC after a translation with vector $\binom{4}{-3}$. Label this Q.

   d Draw the image of ABC after a translation with vector $\binom{-4}{3}$. Label this R.

   e Draw the image of ABC after a translation with vector $\binom{-3}{-2}$. Label this S.

3 Using your diagram from Question **2**, describe the translation that will move

   a P to Q   **b** Q to R   **c** R to S   **d** S to P

   e R to P   **f** S to Q   **g** R to Q   **h** P to S

1 Copy each shape on squared paper and draw its image after a reflection in the given mirror line.

   a

   b

   c

   d

   e

   f

2 **a** Draw a pair of axes, *x*-axis from −5 to 5, *y*-axis from −5 to 5.

  b Draw the triangle with co-ordinates A(2, 2), B(3, 4), C(2, 4).

  c Reflect the triangle ABC in the line $y = x$. Label the image P.

  d Reflect the triangle P in the line $y = -x$. Label the image Q.

  e Reflect triangle Q in the line $y = x$, label it R.

  f Describe the reflection that will move triangle ABC to triangle R.

★**3** Copy this diagram on squared paper.

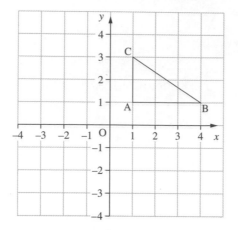

  a Reflect the triangle ABC in the *x*-axis. Label the image R.

  b Reflect the triangle ABC in the *y*-axis. Label the image S.

  c What special name is given to figures that are exactly the same shape and size?

4 **a** Draw a pair of axes with the *x*-axis from −5 to 5 and the *y*-axis from −5 to 5.

  b Draw the triangle with co-ordinates A(1, 1), B(5, 5), C(3, 4).

  c Reflect triangle ABC in the *x*-axis. Label the image P.

  d Reflect triangle P in the *y*-axis. Label the image Q.

  e Reflect triangle Q in the *x*-axis. Label the image R.

  f Describe the reflection that will transform triangle ABC onto triangle R.

HOMEWORK 8D

1 Copy the diagram and rotate the given triangle by

  a $\frac{1}{4}$ turn clockwise about (0, 0)

  b $\frac{1}{2}$ turn clockwise about (0, 2)

  c 90° turn anticlockwise about (−1, 1)

  d 180° turn about (0, 0).

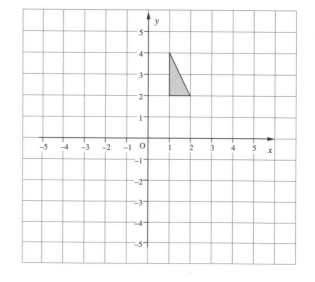

2 Describe the rotation that takes the shaded triangle to
   a triangle A
   b triangle B
   c triangle C
   d triangle D.

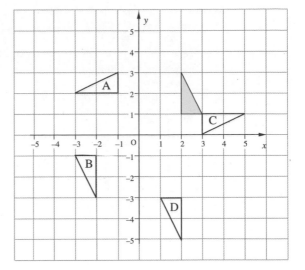

★**3** Copy this T-shape on squared paper.
   a Rotate the shape 90° clockwise about the origin O. Label the image P.
   b Rotate the shape 180° clockwise about the origin O. Label the image Q.
   c Rotate the shape 270° clockwise about the origin O. Label the image R.
   d What rotation takes R back to the original shape?

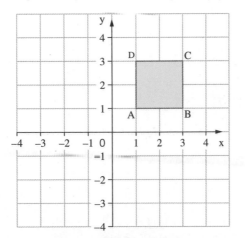

★**4** Copy this square ABCD on squared paper.

   a Write down the co-ordinates of the vertices of the square ABCD.
   b Rotate the square ABCD through 90° clockwise about the origin O. Label the image S. Write down the co-ordinates of the vertices of the square S.
   c Rotate the square ABCD through 180° clockwise about the origin O. Label the image T. Write down the co-ordinates of the vertices of the square T.
   d Rotate the square ABCD through 270° clockwise about the origin O. Label the image U. Write down the co-ordinates of the vertices of the square U.
   e What do you notice about the co-ordinates of the four squares?

1 Copy each figure below with its centre of enlargement, leaving plenty of space for the enlargement. Then enlarge them by the given scale factor, using the ray method.

2 Copy each figure below with its centre of enlargement, leaving plenty of space for the enlargement. Then enlarge them by the given scale factor, using the co-ordinate method.

1 Describe fully the transformation that will move

    a T_1 to T_2 **b** T_1 to T_6 **c** T_2 to T_3 **d** T_6 to T_2

    e T_6 to T_5 **f** T_5 to T_4 **g** T_1 to T_5

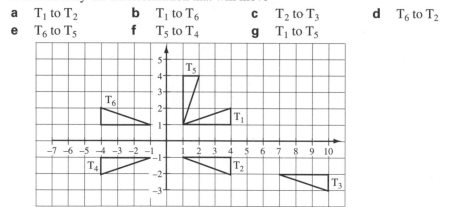

2 **a** Plot a triangle T with vertices (1, 1), (3, 1), (3, 4).
    b Reflect triangle T in the *x*-axis and label the image T_b.
    c Rotate triangle T_b 90° clockwise about the origin and label the image T_c.
    d Reflect triangle T_c in the *x*-axis and label the image T_d.
    e Describe fully the transformation that will move triangle T_d back to triangle T.

★3 The point P(2, 5) is reflected in the *x*-axis, then rotated by 90° clockwise about the origin. What are the co-ordinates of the image of P?

9 Construction

1   Draw a line 8 cm long. Bisect it with a pair of compasses. Check your accuracy by seeing if each half is 4 cm.

2   a   Draw any triangle.
    b   On each side construct the line bisector. All your line bisectors should intersect at the same point.
    c   Use this point as the centre of a circle that only touches each vertex of the triangle. Draw this circle.

3   a   Draw a circle with a radius of about 4 cm.
    b   Draw a quadrilateral such that the vertices (corners) of the quadrilateral are on the circumference of the circle.
    c   Bisect two of the sides of the quadrilateral. Your bisectors should meet at the centre of the circle.

4   a   Draw any angle.
    b   Construct the angle bisector.
    c   Check how accurate you have been by measuring each half.

★5 The diagram shows a park with two ice-cream sellers A and B. People always go to the ice-cream seller nearest to them. Shade the region of the park from which people go to ice-cream seller B.

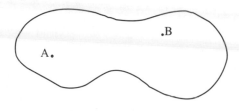

1   Construct these triangles accurately without using a protractor.

2   a   Without using a protractor, construct a square of side 5 cm.
    b   See how accurate you have been by constructing an angle bisector on any of the right-angles and seeing whether this also cuts through the opposite right-angle.

3   With ruler and compasses only, construct an angle of 45°.

4   With ruler and compasses only, construct an angle of 30°.

5 **a** Draw a line 8 cm long. Call it AB.

b At the point A construct an angle of 60°.

c At the point B construct an angle of 45°.

d Label the point where the two lines meet C.

e Measure AC and BC.

★**6** **a** Draw an accurate triangle ABC using only a ruler and compasses.

b Measure the side BC.

HOMEWORK 9C

1 A is a fixed point. Sketch the locus of the point P when AP > 3 cm and AP < 6 cm.

2 A and B are two fixed points 4 cm apart. Sketch the locus of the point P for the following situations:

a AP < BP

b P is always within 3 cm of A and within 2 cm of B.

3 A fly is tethered by a length of spider's web that is 1 m long. Describe the locus that the fly can still buzz about in.

4 ABC is an equilateral triangle of side 4 cm. In each of the following loci, the point P moves only inside the triangle. Sketch the locus in each case.

a AP = BP

b AP < BP

c CP < 2 cm

d CP > 3 cm and BP > 3 cm

5 A wheel rolls around the inside of a square. Sketch the locus of the centre of the wheel.

6 The same wheel rolls around the outside of the square. Sketch the locus of the centre of the wheel.

★**7** Two ships A and B, which are 7 km apart, both ⸱ar a distress signal from a fishing boat. The fishing boat is less than 4 km from ship A and is less than 4.5 km from ship B. A helicopter pilot sees that the fishing boat is nearer to ship A than to ship B. Use accurate construction to show the region which contains the fishing boat. Shade this region.

For questions 1 to 3, you should start by sketching the picture given in each question on a 6 × 6 grid, each square of which is 1 cm by 1 cm. The scale for each question is given.

1   A goat is tethered by a rope, 10 m long, and a stake that is 2 m from each side of a field. What is the locus of the area that the goat can graze? Use a scale of 1 cm : 2 m.

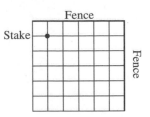

2   A cow is tethered to a rail at the top of a fence 4 m long. The rope is 4 m long. Sketch the area that the cow can graze. Use a scale of 1 cm : 2 m.

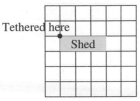

3   A horse is tethered to a corner of a shed, 3 m by 1 m. The rope is 4 m long. Sketch the area that the horse can graze. Use a scale of 1 cm : 1 m.

For questions 4 to 6, you should use a copy of the map on page 50. For each question, trace the map and mark on those points that are relevant to that question.

4   A radio station broadcasts from Birmingham with a range that is just far enough to reach York. Another radio station broadcasts from Glasgow with a range that is just far enough to reach Newcastle.
    a   Sketch the area to which each station can broadcast.
    b   Will the Birmingham station broadcast as far as Norwich?
    c   Will the broadcasts then interfere with each other?

5   An air traffic control centre is to be built in Newcastle. If it has a range of 200 km, will it cover all the area of Britain north of Sheffield and south of Glasgow?

6   A radio transmitter is to be built so that it is the same distance from Exeter, Norwich and Newcastle.
    a   Draw the perpendicular bisectors of the lines joining these three places to find where the station is to be built.
    b   Birmingham has so many radio stations that it cannot have another one within 50 km. Can the transmitter be built?

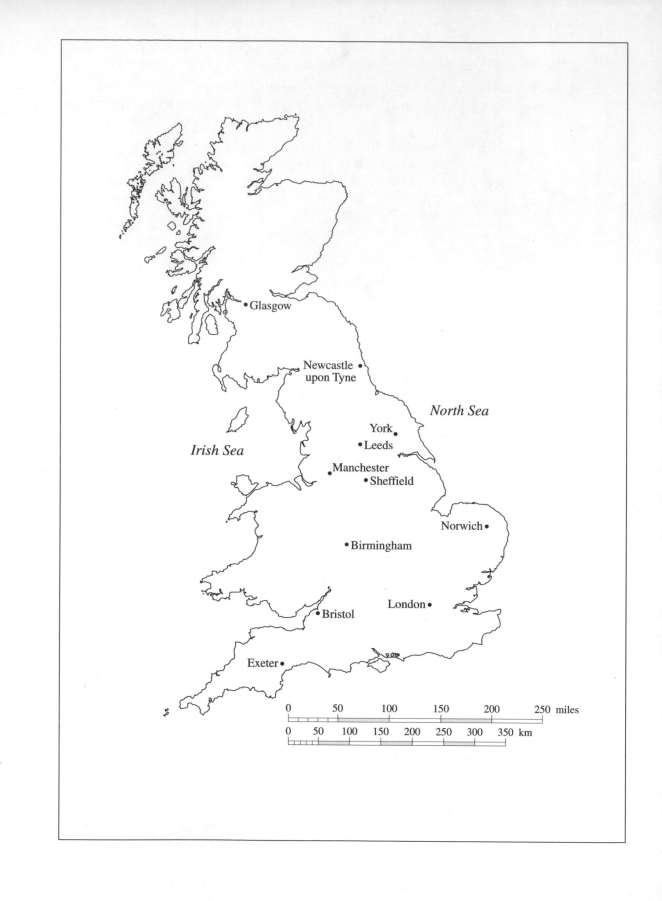

Glasgow

Newcastle
upon Tyne

North Sea

York
Leeds

Irish Sea

Manchester
Sheffield

Norwich

Birmingham

London

Bristol

Exeter

| 0 | 50 | 100 | 150 | 200 | 250 miles |

| 0 | 50 | 100 | 150 | 200 | 250 | 300 | 350 km |

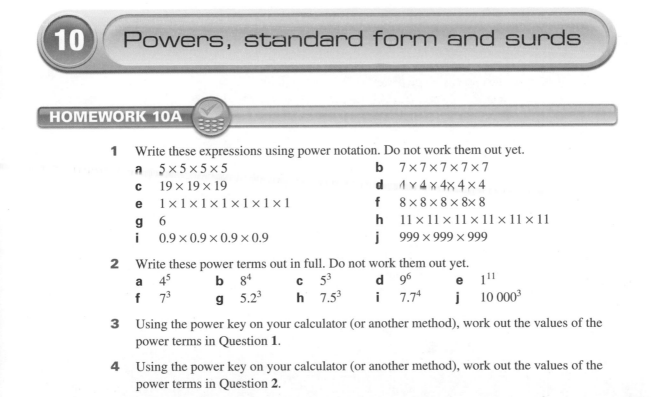

★7 A new mobile telephone mast covers the three towns Alphaville, Beeton, and Ceeton. The position of the three towns is shown. The diagram is drawn to a scale of 1 cm to 10 km.

• Ceeton

• Alphaville

• Beeton

The mast is located within the triangle formed by Alphaville, Beeton, and Ceeton so that it is

i equidistant from Alphaville and Ceeton **ii** 50 km from Beeton.

Construct the position of the mast on the diagram. Mark with an X the position of the mast.

10 Powers, standard form and surds

HOMEWORK 10A

1 Write these expressions using power notation. Do not work them out yet.

 a $5 \times 5 \times 5 \times 5$ **b** $7 \times 7 \times 7 \times 7 \times 7$

 c $19 \times 19 \times 19$ **d** $4 \times 4 \times 4 \times 4 \times 4$

 e $1 \times 1 \times 1 \times 1 \times 1 \times 1 \times 1$ **f** $8 \times 8 \times 8 \times 8 \times 8$

 g 6 **h** $11 \times 11 \times 11 \times 11 \times 11 \times 11$

 i $0.9 \times 0.9 \times 0.9 \times 0.9$ **j** $999 \times 999 \times 999$

2 Write these power terms out in full. Do not work them out yet.

 a 4^5 **b** 8^4 **c** 5^3 **d** 9^6 **e** 1^{11}

 f 7^3 **g** 5.2^3 **h** 7.5^3 **i** 7.7^4 **j** $10\,000^3$

3 Using the power key on your calculator (or another method), work out the values of the power terms in Question **1**.

4 Using the power key on your calculator (or another method), work out the values of the power terms in Question **2**.

5 Without using a calculator, work out the values of these power terms.

    a 7^0 **b** 9^1 **c** 17^0 **d** 1^{91} **e** 10^5

6 Using your calculator, or otherwise, work out the values of these power terms.

    a $(-2)^3$ **b** $(-1)^{11}$ **c** $(-3)^4$ **d** $(-5)^3$ **e** $(-10)^6$

7 Without using a calculator, write down the answers to these.

    a $(-4)^2$ **b** $(-5)^3$ **c** $(-3)^4$ **d** $(-2)^5$ **e** $(-1)^6$

HOMEWORK 10B

1 Write down each of these in fraction form.

    a 5^{-2} **b** 4^{-1} **c** 10^{-3} **f** 3^{-3} **g** x^{-2} **h** $5t^{-1}$

2 Write down each of these in negative index form.

    a $\dfrac{1}{2^4}$ **b** $\dfrac{1}{7}$ **c** $\dfrac{1}{x^2}$

3 Change each of the following expressions into an index form of the type shown.

    a All of the form 2^n **i** 32   **ii** $\frac{1}{4}$

    b All of the form 10^n **i** 10 000   **ii** $\frac{1}{100}$

    c All of the form 5^n **i** 625   **ii** $\frac{1}{125}$

4 Find the value of each of the following, where the letters have the given values.

    a Where $x = 3$ **i** x^2 **ii** $4x^{-1}$

    b Where $t = 5$ **i** t^{-2} **ii** $5t^{-4}$

    c Where $m = 2$ **i** m^{-3} **ii** $4m^{-2}$

★5 $a = 3$ and $b = 2$. Calculate the value of

    a $3a^{-1} + 2b^{-2}$, giving your answer as a fraction in its simplest form.

    b $a^{-2} + b^{-3}$, giving your answer as a fraction in its simplest form.

HOMEWORK 10C

1 Write these as single powers of 7.

    a $7^3 \times 7^2$ **b** $7^3 \times 7^6$ **c** $7^4 \times 7^3$ **d** 7×7^5 **e** $7^5 \times 7^9$ **f** 7×7^7

2 Write these as single powers of 5.

    a $5^6 \div 5^2$ **b** $5^8 \div 5^2$ **c** $5^4 \div 5^3$ **d** $5^5 \div 5^5$ **e** $5^6 \div 5^4$

3 Simplify these and write them as single powers of a.

    a $a^2 \times a$ **b** $a^3 \times a^2$ **c** $a^4 \times a^3$ **d** $a^6 \div a^2$ **e** $a^3 \div a$ **f** $a^5 \div a^4$

4 Simplify these expressions.

    a $3a^4 \times 5a^2$ **b** $3a^4 \times 7a$ **c** $5a^4 \times 6a^2$ **d** $3a^2 \times 4a^7$

    e $5a^4 \times 5a^2 \times 5a^2$

5 Simplify these expressions.

    a $8a^5 \div 2a^2$ **b** $12a^7 \div 4a^2$ **c** $25a^6 \div 5a$ **d** $48a^8 \div 6a^{-1}$

    e $24a^6 \div 8a^{-2}$ **f** $36a \div 6a^5$

6 Simplify these expressions.

    a $3a^3b^2 \times 4a^3b$ **b** $7a^3b^5 \times 2ab^3$ **c** $4a^3b^5 \times 5a^4b^{-1}$

    d $12a^3b^5 \div 4ab$ **e** $24a^3b^5 \div 6a^2b^{-3}$

7 Use the general rule for dividing powers of the same number
$$a^x \div a^y = a^{x-y}$$
to prove that any number raised to the power −1 is the reciprocal of that number.

HOMEWORK 10D

Evaluate the following.

1 $36^{\frac{1}{2}}$ **2** $144^{\frac{1}{2}}$ **3** $25^{\frac{1}{2}}$ **4** $196^{\frac{1}{2}}$ **5** $8^{\frac{1}{3}}$ **6** $125^{\frac{1}{3}}$

7 $32^{-\frac{1}{5}}$ **8** $144^{-\frac{1}{2}}$ **9** $27^{-\frac{1}{3}}$ **10** $(\frac{25}{81})^{\frac{1}{2}}$ **11** $(\frac{81}{36})^{\frac{1}{2}}$ **12** $(\frac{36}{64})^{\frac{1}{2}}$

13 $(\frac{8}{27})^{\frac{1}{3}}$ **14** $(\frac{16}{625})^{\frac{1}{4}}$ **15** $(\frac{4}{9})^{-\frac{1}{2}}$ **16** $(\frac{16}{25})^{-\frac{1}{2}}$ **17** $(\frac{8}{27})^{-\frac{1}{3}}$

★**18** Evaluate the following.
   a $81^{\frac{1}{2}}$ **b** $64^{\frac{1}{3}}$ **c** $64^{-\frac{1}{3}}$

HOMEWORK 10E

1 Evaluate the following.
   a $16^{\frac{3}{4}}$ **b** $125^{\frac{4}{3}}$ **c** $81^{\frac{3}{4}}$

2 Rewrite the following in index form.
   a $\sqrt[4]{t^3}$ **b** $\sqrt[5]{m^2}$

3 Evaluate the following.
   a $27^{\frac{2}{3}}$ **b** $8^{\frac{4}{3}}$ **c** $36^{\frac{3}{2}}$ **d** $81^{1.25}$

4 **a** Draw the graph of $y = 2^x$ for $x = -2$ to 5.
   b Use your graph to estimate the value of $2^{\frac{5}{2}}$.

5 Using a trial-and-improvement method, or otherwise, solve these equations.
   a $6^x = 60$ **b** $10^x = 2$ (You could try to use the **power** key on your calculator.)

★**6** **a** Evaluate $8^{\frac{1}{3}}$.   **b** Write $16^{-\frac{1}{4}} \times 2^{-3}$ as a power of 2.
   c Given that $32^y = 2$, find the value of y.

HOMEWORK 10F

1 Evaluate the following.
   a 3.5×100 **b** 2.15×10 **c** 6.74×1000 **d** 4.63×10
   e 30.145×10 **f** 78.56×1000 **g** 6.42×10^2 **h** 0.067×10
   i 0.085×10^3 **j** 0.798×10^5 **k** 0.658×1000 **l** 215.3×10^2
   m 0.889×10^6 **n** 352.147×10^2 **o** 37.2841×10^3 **p** 34.28×10^6

2 Evaluate the following.
   a $4538 \div 100$ **b** $435 \div 10$ **c** $76459 \div 1000$ **d** $643.7 \div 10$
   e $4228.7 \div 100$ **f** $278.4 \div 1000$ **g** $246.5 \div 10^2$ **h** $76.3 \div 10$
   i $76 \div 10^3$ **j** $897 \div 10^5$ **k** $86.5 \div 1000$ **l** $1.5 \div 10^2$
   m $0.8799 \div 10^6$ **n** $23.4 \div 10^2$ **o** $7654 \div 10^3$ **p** $73.2 \div 10^6$

3 Evaluate the following.
   a 400×300 **b** 50×4000 **c** 70×200 **d** 30×700
   e $(30)^2$ **f** $(50)^3$ **g** $(200)^2$ **h** 40×150
   i 70×200 **j** 60×5000 **k** 30×250 **l** 700×200

4 Evaluate the following.

a	$4000 \div 800$	**b**	$9000 \div 30$	**c**	$7000 \div 200$	**d**	$8000 \div 200$
e	$2100 \div 700$	**f**	$9000 \div 60$	**g**	$700 \div 50$	**h**	$3500 \div 70$
i	$3000 \div 500$	**j**	$30\,000 \div 2000$	**k**	$5600 \div 1400$	**l**	$6000 \div 30$

5 Evaluate the following.

a	7.3×10^2	**b**	3.29×10^5	**c**	7.94×10^3	**d**	6.8×10^7
e	$3.46 \div 10^2$	**f**	$5.07 \div 10^4$	**g**	$2.3 \div 10^4$	**h**	$0.89 \div 10^3$

HOMEWORK 10G

1 Write these standard form numbers out in full.

a	3.5×10^2	**b**	4.15×10	**c**	5.7×10^{-3}	**d**	1.46×10
e	3.89×10^{-2}	**f**	4.6×10^3	**g**	2.7×10^2	**h**	8.6×10
i	4.6×10^3	**j**	3.97×10^5	**k**	3.65×10^{-3}	**l**	7.05×10^2

2 Write these numbers in standard form.

a	780	**b**	0.435	**c**	$67\,800$	**d**	$7\,400\,000\,000$
e	$30\,780\,000\,000$	**f**	$0.000\,427\,8$	**g**	6450	**h**	0.047
i	$0.000\,12$	**j**	96.43	**k**	74.78	**l**	$0.004\,157\,8$

In Questions **3** to **7**, write the appropriate numbers given in each question in standard form.

3 In 1990 there were 24 673 000 vehicles licensed in the UK.

4 In 2001 Keith Gordon was one of 15 282 runners to complete the Boston Marathon.

5 In 1990 the total number of passenger kilometres on the British roads was 613 000 000 000.

6 The Sun is 93 million miles away from Earth. The next nearest star to the Earth is Proxima Centuri which is about 24 million million miles away.

7 A scientist was working with a new particle reported to weigh only 0.000 000 000 000 65 g.

HOMEWORK 10H

1 Find the results of the following, leaving your answers in standard form.

    a $(4 \times 10^6) \times (7 \times 10^9)$ **b** $(7 \times 10^5) \times (5 \times 10^7)$

    c $(3 \times 10^{-5}) \times (8 \times 10^8)$ **d** $(2.1 \times 10^7) \times (5 \times 10^{-8})$

2 Find the results of the following, leaving your answers in standard form.

    a $(9 \times 10^8) \div (3 \times 10^4)$ **b** $(2.7 \times 10^7) \div (9 \times 10^3)$

    c $(5.5 \times 10^4) \div (1.1 \times 10^{-2})$ **d** $(4.2 \times 10^{-9}) \div (3 \times 10^{-8})$

3 Find the results of the following, leaving your answers in standard form.

    a $\dfrac{8 \times 10^9}{4 \times 10^7}$ **b** $\dfrac{12 \times 10^6}{3 \times 10^4}$ **c** $\dfrac{2.8 \times 10^7}{7 \times 10^{-4}}$

4 $p = 8 \times 10^5$ and $q = 2 \times 10^7$

Find the value of the following, leaving your answer in standard form.

    a $p \times q$ **b** $p \div q$ **c** $p + q$ **d** $q - p$ **e** $\dfrac{q}{p}$

5 $p = 2 \times 10^{-2}$ and $q = 4 \times 10^{-3}$

    a $p \times q$ **b** $p \div q$ **c** $p + q$ **d** $q - p$ **e** $\dfrac{q}{p}$

1 Work out each of these fractions as a decimal. Give them as terminating decimals or recurring decimals as appropriate.

    a $\frac{3}{4}$ **b** $\frac{1}{15}$ **c** $\frac{1}{25}$ **d** $\frac{1}{11}$ **e** $\frac{1}{20}$

2 There are several patterns to be found in recurring decimals. For example,

    $\frac{1}{13} = 0.076923076923076923076923\ldots$; $\frac{2}{13} = 0.153846153846153846153846\ldots$

    $\frac{3}{13} = 0.230769230769230769230769\ldots$ and so on

    a Write down the decimals for $\frac{4}{13}, \frac{5}{13}, \frac{6}{13}, \frac{7}{13}, \frac{8}{13}, \frac{9}{13}, \frac{10}{13}, \frac{11}{13}, \frac{12}{13}$ to 24 decimal places.

    b What do you notice?

3 Write each of these fractions as a decimal. Use this to write the list in order of size, smallest first.

    $\frac{2}{9}$ $\frac{1}{5}$ $\frac{23}{100}$ $\frac{2}{7}$ $\frac{3}{11}$

4 Convert each of these terminating decimals to a fraction.

    a 0.57   **b** 0.275   **c** 0.85   **d** 0.06   **e** 3.65

5 $x = 0.0242\,424\ldots$

    a What is $100x$?

    b By subtracting the original value from your answer to part **a**, work out the value of $99x$.

    c Multiply both sides by 10 to get $990x$ and eliminate the decimal on the right-hand side.

    d Divide both sides by 990.

    e What is x as a fraction expressed in its lowest terms?

6 Convert each of these recurring decimals to a fraction.

    a $0.\dot{7}$ **b** $0.5\dot{7}$ **c** $0.\dot{5}\dot{4}$ **d** $0.2\dot{7}\dot{5}$

    e $2.\dot{5}$ **f** $2.3\dot{6}$ **g** $0.06\dot{3}$ **h** $2.0\dot{7}\dot{5}$

★7 **a** Write 1.7 as a rational number in the form $\frac{a}{b}$, where a and b are whole numbers.

    Given that $n = 1.\dot{7}$

    b **i** Write down the value of $10n$.

        ii Hence write down the value of $9n$.

        iii Express n as a rational number, in the form $\frac{a}{b}$, where a and b are whole numbers.

1 Work out each of the following in simplified form.

    a $\sqrt{3} \times \sqrt{4}$ **b** $\sqrt{5} \times \sqrt{7}$ **c** $\sqrt{5} \times \sqrt{5}$ **d** $\sqrt{2} \times \sqrt{32}$

2 Work out each of the following in surd form.

    a $\sqrt{15} \div \sqrt{5}$ **b** $\sqrt{18} \div \sqrt{2}$ **c** $\sqrt{32} \div \sqrt{2}$ **d** $\sqrt{12} \div \sqrt{8}$

3 Work out each of the following in surd form.

    a $\sqrt{3} \times \sqrt{3} \times \sqrt{2}$ **b** $\sqrt{5} \times \sqrt{5} \times \sqrt{15}$ **c** $\sqrt{2} \times \sqrt{8} \times \sqrt{8}$ **d** $\sqrt{2} \times \sqrt{8} \times \sqrt{5}$

4 Work out each of the following in surd form.

    a $\sqrt{3} \times \sqrt{8} \div \sqrt{2}$ **b** $\sqrt{15} \times \sqrt{3} \div \sqrt{5}$ **c** $\sqrt{8} \times \sqrt{8} \div \sqrt{2}$ **d** $\sqrt{3} \times \sqrt{27} \div \sqrt{3}$

5 Simplify each of the following surds into the form $a\sqrt{b}$.

    a $\sqrt{90}$ **b** $\sqrt{32}$ **c** $\sqrt{63}$ **d** $\sqrt{300}$

    e $\sqrt{150}$ **f** $\sqrt{270}$ **g** $\sqrt{96}$ **h** $\sqrt{125}$

6 Simplify each of these.

   a $2\sqrt{32} \times 5\sqrt{2}$ **b** $4\sqrt{8} \times 2\sqrt{2}$ **c** $4\sqrt{12} \times 5\sqrt{3}$ **d** $3\sqrt{6} \times 2\sqrt{6}$

   e $2\sqrt{5} \times 5\sqrt{3}$ **f** $2\sqrt{3} \times 3\sqrt{3}$ **g** $2\sqrt{2} \times 3\sqrt{8}$ **h** $2\sqrt{3} \times 2\sqrt{27}$

   i $8\sqrt{24} \div 2\sqrt{3}$ **j** $3\sqrt{27} \div \sqrt{3}$ **k** $5\sqrt{18} \div \sqrt{2}$ **l** $2\sqrt{32} \div 4\sqrt{8}$

   m $5\sqrt{2} \times \sqrt{8} \div 2\sqrt{2}$ **n** $3\sqrt{15} \times \sqrt{3} \div \sqrt{5}$ **o** $2\sqrt{24} \times 5\sqrt{3} \div 2\sqrt{8}$

7 Find the value of a that makes each of these surds true.

   a $\sqrt{5} \times \sqrt{a} = 20$ **b** $\sqrt{3} \times \sqrt{a} = 12$ **c** $\sqrt{5} \times 4\sqrt{a} = 20$

8 The following rule is not true. Try a numerical example to show this.

   $\sqrt{(a^2 + b^2)} = a + b$

9 Simplify the following.

   a $\left(\dfrac{\sqrt{2}}{3}\right)^2$ **b** $\left(\dfrac{4}{\sqrt{3}}\right)^2$

★10 Simplify the following.

   a $\sqrt{32} + \sqrt{8}$ **b** $\sqrt{32} \times \sqrt{8}$ **c** $\sqrt{27} \times \sqrt{18} \div \sqrt{3}$

HOMEWORK 10K

1 Show that

   a $(3 + \sqrt{5})(2 + \sqrt{5}) = 11 + 5\sqrt{5}$ **b** $(3 - \sqrt{2})(3 + \sqrt{2}) = 7$

2 Expand and simplify where possible.

   a $\sqrt{5}(3 - \sqrt{2})$ **b** $\sqrt{8}(3 - 4\sqrt{2})$ **c** $3\sqrt{8}(2\sqrt{2} + 4)$

   d $(2 + \sqrt{3})(1 - \sqrt{3})$ **e** $(3 + \sqrt{5})(2 - \sqrt{5})$ **f** $(3 - \sqrt{2})(4 + 2\sqrt{2})$

3 Work out the missing lengths in these triangles, simplifying the answer where possible.

4 Calculate the area of these rectangles, simplifying your answer where possible.

5 Rationalise the denominators of these expressions.

   a $\dfrac{1}{\sqrt{7}}$ **b** $\dfrac{1}{\sqrt{8}}$ **c** $\dfrac{2}{\sqrt{5}}$ **d** $\dfrac{1}{2\sqrt{2}}$

   e $\dfrac{5\sqrt{3}}{\sqrt{27}}$ **f** $\dfrac{\sqrt{8}}{\sqrt{3}}$ **g** $\dfrac{1 + \sqrt{3}}{\sqrt{3}}$ **h** $\dfrac{3 - \sqrt{2}}{\sqrt{8}}$

6 **a** Expand and simplify

     i $(5 + \sqrt{3})(5 - \sqrt{3})$ **ii** $(6 - \sqrt{2})(6 + \sqrt{2})$

   b Use your results from part **a** to rationalise the denominators of

     i $\dfrac{5}{5 - \sqrt{3}}$ **ii** $\dfrac{2 + \sqrt{3}}{6 + \sqrt{2}}$

★7 **a** If $m = 5$ and $n = -7$, write down the exact value of the following, leaving your answers as integers or fractions if you can, otherwise as an irrational number.

     i $m^2 - n^2$ **ii** $m^{\frac{1}{2}}$ **iii** n^{-3}

   b Simplify $(4 - \sqrt{5})^2$ as far as possible, without using a calculator.

11 Statistics 1

1 **a** For each set of data find the mode, the median and the mean.

    i   6, 4, 5, 6, 2, 3, 2, 4, 5, 6, 1

    ii   14, 15, 15, 16, 15, 15, 14, 16, 15, 16, 15

    iii 31, 34, 33, 32, 46, 29, 30, 32, 31, 32, 33

  b For each set of data decide which average is the best one to use and give a reason.

2 A supermarket sells oranges in bags of ten.

The weights of each orange in a selected bag were as follows:

    134 g, 135 g, 142 g, 153 g, 156 g, 132 g, 135 g, 140 g, 148 g, 155 g

  a Find the mode, the median and the mean for the weight of the oranges.

  b The supermarket wanted to state the average weight on each bag they sold. Which of the three averages would you advise the supermarket to use? Explain why.

★3 The weights, in kilograms, of players in a school football team are as follows:

    68, 72, 74, 68, 71, 78, 53, 67, 72, 77, 70

  a Find the median weight of the team.

  b Find the mean weight of the team.

  c Which average is the better one to use? Explain why.

★4 Jez is a member of a pub quiz team and, in the last eight games, his total points were:

    62, 58, 24, 47, 64, 52, 60, 65

  a Find the median for the number of points he scored over the eight weeks.

  b Find the mean for the number of points he scored over the eight weeks.

  c The team captain wanted to know the average for each member of the team. Which average would Jez use? Give a reason for your answer.

1 Find **i** the mode, **ii** the median and **iii** the mean from each frequency table below.

  a A survey of the collar sizes of all the male staff in a school gave these results.

Collar size	12	13	14	15	16	17	18
Number of staff	1	3	12	21	22	8	1

  b A survey of the number of TVs in pupils' homes gave these results.

Number of TVs	1	2	3	4	5	6	7
Frequency	12	17	30	71	96	74	25

2 A survey of the number of pets in each family of a school gave these results.

Number of pets	0	1	2	3	4	5
Frequency	28	114	108	16	15	8

  a Each child at the school is shown in the data, how many children are at the school?

  b Calculate the median number of pets in a family.

  c How many families have less than the median number of pets?

  d Calculate the mean number of pets in a family. Give your answer to 1 dp.

1   Find for each table of values given below
    i   the modal group   **ii**   an estimate for the mean.

a

Score	0 – 20	21 – 40	41 – 60	61 – 80	81 – 100
Frequency	9	13	21	34	17

b

Cost (£)	0.00 – 10.00	10.01 – 20.00	20.01 – 30.00	30.01 – 40.00	40.01 – 60.00
Frequency	9	17	27	21	14

2   A survey was made to see how long casualty patients had to wait before seeing a doctor. The following table summarises the results for one shift.

Time (minutes)	0 – 10	11 – 20	21 – 30	31 – 40	41 – 50	51 – 60	61 – 70
Frequency	1	12	24	15	13	9	5

a   How many patients were seen by a doctor in the survey of this shift?
b   Estimate the mean waiting time taken per patient.
c   Which average would the hospital use for the average waiting time?
d   What percentage of patients did the doctors see within the hour?

1   **a**   The table shows the ages of 300 people at the cinema.

Age, x years	$0 \leqslant x < 10$	$10 \leqslant x < 20$	$20 \leqslant x < 30$	$30 \leqslant x < 40$	$40 \leqslant x < 50$
Frequency	25	85	115	45	30

   Draw a histogram to show the data.
b   At another film show this was the distribution of ages.

Age, x years	$20 \leqslant x < 30$	$30 \leqslant x < 40$	$40 \leqslant x < 50$	$50 \leqslant x < 60$	$60 \leqslant x < 70$
Frequency	35	120	130	50	15

   Draw a histogram to show this data.
c   Comment on the differences between the distributions.

2   The table shows the times taken by 50 children to complete a multiplication square.

Time, s seconds	$10 \leqslant s < 20$	$20 \leqslant s < 30$	$30 \leqslant s < 40$	$40 \leqslant s < 50$	$50 \leqslant s < 60$
Frequency	3	9	28	6	4

a   Draw a frequency polygon for this data.
b   Calculate an estimate of the mean of the data.

★3   The waiting times for customers at a supermarket checkout are shown in the table.
   a   Draw a histogram of these waiting times.
   b   Estimate the mean waiting time.

Waiting time (minutes)	Frequency
$0 \leqslant x < 2$	15
$2 \leqslant x < 4$	7
$4 \leqslant x < 6$	12
$6 \leqslant x < 8$	15
$8 \leqslant x < 10$	12

1 a The table shows the ages of 300 people at the cinema.

Age, x years	$0 \leqslant x < 10$	$10 \leqslant x < 20$	$20 \leqslant x < 30$	$30 \leqslant x < 40$	$40 \leqslant x < 50$
Frequency	25	85	115	45	30

Draw a histogram to show the data.

b At another film show this was the distribution of ages

Age, x years	$20 \leqslant x < 30$	$30 \leqslant x < 40$	$40 \leqslant x < 50$	$50 \leqslant x < 60$	$60 \leqslant x < 70$
Frequency	35	120	130	50	15

Draw a histogram to show this data.

c Comment on the differences between the distributions.

2 The table shows the times taken by 50 children to complete a multiplication square.

Time, s seconds	$10 \leqslant s < 20$	$20 \leqslant s < 30$	$30 \leqslant s < 40$	$40 \leqslant s < 50$	$50 \leqslant s < 60$
Frequency	3	9	28	6	4

a Draw a histogram to show the data.
b Calculate an estimate of the mean of the data.
c Draw a vertical line on the histogram at the mean value.
d What is the significance of this line in relation to the size of the bars of the histogram?

3 For the histogram below
  a write out the frequency diagram
  b calculate an estimate of the mean
     of the distribution.

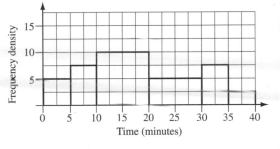

★4 The waiting times for customers at a supermarket checkout are shown in the table.
  a Draw a histogram of these waiting times.
  b Show an estimate of the median on your histogram. Show your working.

Waiting time (minutes)	Frequency
$0 \leqslant x < 1$	15
$1 \leqslant x < 3$	7
$3 \leqslant x < 4$	12
$4 \leqslant x < 5$	15
$5 \leqslant x < 10$	12

1 The following table shows the daily sales of newspapers at a garage for a month.

Sun	Mon	Tue	Wed	Thur	Fri	Sat
125	87	63	91	42	115	169
112	74	43	68	32	154	147
148	98	72	71	56	122	153
110	129	87	75	47	143	194

Make a table showing the moving average using a seven-day span, and draw a graph to show the trend of newspaper sales over the month.

2 Geoff scored the following runs in the cricket season.

31	15	58	114	36	0	98	128	77	5
103	89	51	23	39	86	74	152	107	76

   a Calculate the three innings moving average for the data and plot this on a graph.

   b Comment on the scores through the season.

HOMEWORK 11G

1 'People like the DVD rental shop to be open 24 hours a day.'

   a To see whether this statement is true, design a data collection sheet which will allow you to capture data while standing outside a video hire centre.

   b Does it matter at which time you collect your data?

2 The youth club wanted to know which types of activities it should plan, e.g. craft, swimming, squash, walking, disco etc.

   a Design a data collection sheet which you could use to ask the pupils in your school which activities they would want in a youth club.

   b Invent the first 30 entries on the chart.

★3 What types of film do your age group watch at the cinema the most? Is it comedy, romance, sci-fi, action, suspense or something else?

   a Design a data collection sheet to be used in a survey of your age group.

   b Invent the first thirty entries on your sheet.

HOMEWORK 11H

1 Design a questionnaire to test the following statement.
'Young people aged 16 and under will not tell their parents when they have been drinking alcohol, but the over 16s will always let their parents know.'

★2 'Boys will use the Internet almost everyday but girls will only use it about once a week.'
Design a questionnaire to test this statement.

★3 Design a questionnaire to test the following hypothesis.
'When you are in your twenties, you watch less TV than any other age group.'

4 While on holiday in Wales, I noticed that in the supermarkets there were a lot more women than men, and even then, the only men I did see were over 65.

   a Write down a hypothesis from the above observation.

   b Design a questionnaire to test your hypothesis.

HOMEWORK 11I

1 For a school project you have been asked to do a presentation of the timing of the school day. You decide to interview a sample of pupils. How will you choose those you wish to interview if you want your results to be reliable? Give three reasons for your decisions.

2 Comment on the reliability of the following ways of finding a sample.

   a Asking the year 11 Religious Education option class about religion.

   b Find out how many homes have microwaves by asking the first 100 pupils who walk through the school gates.

   c Find the most popular Playstation game by asking a Year 7 form which their favourite is.

3 Comment on the way the following samples have been taken. For those that are not satisfactory, suggest a better way to find a more reliable sample.

    a Bill wanted to find out what proportion of his school went to the cinema, so he obtained an alphabetical list of students and sent a questionnaire to every tenth person on the list.

    b The council wants to know about sports facilities in an area so they sent a survey team to the local shopping centre one Monday morning.

    c A political party wanted to know how much support they had in an area so they rang 500 people from the phone book in the evening.

4 Shameela made a survey of pupils in her school. The size of each year group in the school is shown below.

Claire took a sample of 150 pupils.

    a Explain why this is a suitable size of sample.

Year	Boys	Girls	Total
7	154	137	291
8	162	156	318
9	134	160	294
10	153	156	309
11	130	140	270
Total	733	749	1482

    b Draw up a table showing how many pupils of each sex and year she should ask if she wants to obtain a stratified sample.

★**5** A train company attempted to estimate the number of people who travel by train in a certain town. They telephoned 200 people in the town one evening and asked, 'Have you travelled by train in the last week?' 32 people said 'Yes.' The train company concluded that 16% of the town's population travel by train. Give three criticisms of this method of estimation.

12   Algebra 2

HOMEWORK 12A

Expand the following expressions.

1 $(x + 2)(x + 5)$ **2** $(t + 3)(t + 2)$ **3** $(w + 4)(w + 1)$

4 $(m + 6)(m + 2)$ **5** $(k + 2)(k + 4)$ **6** $(a + 3)(a + 1)$

7 $(x + 3)(x - 1)$ **8** $(t + 6)(t - 4)$ **9** $(w + 2)(w - 3)$

10 $(f + 1)(f - 4)$ **11** $(g + 2)(g - 5)$ **12** $(y + 5)(y - 2)$

13 $(x - 4)(x + 3)$ **14** $(p - 3)(p + 2)$ **15** $(k - 5)(k + 1)$

16 $(y - 3)(y + 6)$ **17** $(a - 2)(a + 4)$ **18** $(t - 4)(t + 5)$

19 $(x - 3)(x - 2)$ **20** $(r - 4)(r - 1)$ **21** $(m - 1)(m - 7)$

22 $(g - 5)(g - 3)$ **23** $(h - 6)(h - 2)$ **24** $(n - 2)(n - 8)$

25 $(4 + x)(3 + x)$ **26** $(5 + t)(4 - t)$ **27** $(2 - b)(6 + b)$

28 $(7 - y)(5 - y)$ **29** $(3 + p)(p - 2)$ **30** $(3 - k)(k - 5)$

Expand the following expressions.

1 $(3x + 4)(4x + 2)$ **2** $(2y + 1)(3y + 2)$ **3** $(4t + 2)(3t + 6)$

4 $(3t + 2)(2t - 1)$ **5** $(6m + 1)(3m - 2)$ **6** $(5k + 3)(4k - 3)$

7 $(4p - 5)(3p + 4)$ **8** $(6w + 1)(3w + 4)$ **9** $(3a - 4)(5a + 1)$

10 $(5r - 2)(3r - 1)$ **11** $(4g - 1)(3g - 2)$ **12** $(3d - 2)(4d + 1)$

13 $(3 + 4p)(5 + 4p)$ **14** $(3 + 2t)(5 + 3t)$ **15** $(2 + 5p)(3p + 1)$

16 $(7 + 4t)(3 - 2t)$ **17** $(5 + 2n)(4 - n)$ **18** $(3 + 4f)(5f - 1)$

19 $(2 - 3q)(5 + 4q)$ **20** $(3 - p)(2 + 3p)$ **21** $(5 - 3t)(4t + 1)$

22 $(5 - 4r)(3 - 4r)$ **23** $(4 - x)(1 - 5x)$ **24** $(2 - 7m)(2m - 3)$

25 $(x + y)(3x + 5y)$ **26** $(4y + t)(3y - 4t)$ **27** $(5x - 3y)(5x + y)$

28 $(x - 2y)(x - 3y)$ **29** $(4m - 3p)(m + 5p)$ **30** $(t - 4k)(3t - k)$

Try to spot the pattern in each of the following expressions so that you can immediately write down the expansion.

1 $(x + 1)(x - 1)$ **2** $(t + 2)(t - 2)$ **3** $(y + 3)(y - 3)$

4 $(2m + 3)(2m - 3)$ **5** $(4k - 3)(4k + 3)$ **6** $(5h - 1)(5h + 1)$

7 $(3 + 2x)(3 - 2x)$ **8** $(7 + 2t)(7 - 2t)$ **9** $(4 - 5y)(4 + 5y)$

10 $(a + b)(a - b)$ **11** $(3t + k)(3t - k)$ **12** $(m - 3p)(m + 3p)$

13 $(8k + g)(8k - g)$ **14** $(ac + bd)(ac - bd)$ **15** $(x^2 + y^2)(x^2 - y^2)$

Expand the following squares.

1 $(x + 4)^2$ **2** $(m + 3)^2$ **3** $(5 + t)^2$ **4** $(2 + p)^2$

5 $(m - 2)^2$ **6** $(t - 4)^2$ **7** $(3 - m)^2$ **8** $(6 - k)^2$

9 $(2x + 1)^2$ **10** $(3t + 2)^2$ **11** $(1 + 4y)^2$ **12** $(2 + m)^2$

13 $(3t - 2)^2$ **14** $(2x - 1)^2$ **15** $(1 - 4t)^2$ **16** $(5 - 4r)^2$

17 $(a + b)^2$ **18** $(x - y)^2$ **19** $(3t + y)^2$ **20** $(m - 2n)^2$

21 $(x + 3)^2 - 4$ **22** $(x - 4)^2 - 25$ **23** $(x + 5)^2 - 36$ **24** $(x - 1)^2 - 1$

Factorise the following.

1 $x^2 + 7x + 6$ 2 $t^2 + 4t + 4$ 3 $m^2 + 11m + 10$ 4 $k^2 + 11k + 24$

5 $p^2 + 10p + 24$ 6 $r^2 + 11r + 18$ 7 $w^2 + 9w + 18$ 8 $x^2 + 8x + 12$

9 $a^2 + 13a + 12$ 10 $k^2 - 10k + 21$ 11 $f^2 - 22f + 21$ 12 $b^2 + 35b + 96$

13 $t^2 + 5t + 6$ 14 $m^2 - 5m + 4$ 15 $p^2 - 7p + 10$ 16 $x^2 - 13x + 36$

17 $c^2 - 12c + 32$ 18 $t^2 - 15t + 36$ 19 $y^2 - 14y + 48$ 20 $j^2 - 19j + 48$

21 $p^2 + 8p + 15$ 22 $y^2 + y - 6$ 23 $t^2 + 7t - 8$ 24 $x^2 + 9x - 10$

25 $m^2 - m - 12$ 26 $r^2 + 6r - 7$ 27 $n^2 - 7n - 18$ 28 $m^2 - 20m - 44$

29 $w^2 - 5w - 24$ 30 $t^2 + t - 90$ 31 $x^2 - x - 72$ 32 $t^2 - 18t - 63$

33 $d^2 - 2d + 1$ 34 $y^2 + 29y + 100$ 35 $t^2 - 10t + 16$ 36 $m^2 - 30m + 81$

37 $x^2 - 30x + 144$ 38 $d^2 - 4d - 12$ 39 $t^2 + t - 20$ 40 $q^2 + q - 56$

41 $p^2 - p - 2$ 42 $v^2 - 2v - 35$ 43 $t^2 - 4t + 3$ 44 $m^2 + 3m - 4$

Each of these is the difference of two squares. Factorise them.

1 $x^2 - 81$ 2 $t^2 - 36$ 3 $4 - x^2$ 4 $81 - t^2$

5 $k^2 - 400$ 6 $64 - y^2$ 7 $x^2 - y^2$ 8 $a^2 - 9b^2$

9 $9x^2 - 25y^2$ 10 $9x^2 - 16$ 11 $100t^2 - 4w^2$ 12 $36a^2 - 49b^2$

★13 Simplify $\dfrac{2a - 3}{4a^2 - 9}$

Factorise the following expressions.

1 $3x^2 + 4x + 1$ 2 $3x^2 - 2x - 1$ 3 $4x^2 + 8x + 3$ 4 $2x^2 + 7x + 3$

5 $15x^2 + 13x + 2$ 6 $4x^2 + 4x - 3$ 7 $6x^2 - 7x + 2$ 8 $8x^2 - 8x - 6$

9 $8x^2 - 13x - 6$ 10 $6x^2 - 13x + 2$

★11 Factorise   a $6x^2 - 2x$ b $6x^2 + 11x - 2$

Solve these equations.

1 $(x + 3)(x + 2) = 0$ 2 $(t + 4)(t + 1) = 0$ 3 $(a + 5)(a + 3) = 0$

4 $(x + 4)(x - 1) = 0$ 5 $(x + 2)(x - 5) = 0$ 6 $(t + 3)(t - 4) = 0$

7 $(x - 2)(x + 1) = 0$ 8 $(x - 1)(x + 4) = 0$ 9 $(a - 6)(a + 5) = 0$

10 $(x - 2)(x - 5) = 0$ 11 $(x - 2)(x - 1) = 0$ 12 $(a - 2)(a - 6) = 0$

First factorise, then solve these equations.

13 $x^2 + 6x + 5 = 0$ **14** $x^2 + 9x + 18 = 0$ **15** $x^2 - 7x + 8 = 0$

16 $x^2 - 4x + 21 = 0$ **17** $x^2 + 3x - 10 = 0$ **18** $x^2 + 2x - 15 = 0$

19 $t^2 - 4t - 12 = 0$ **20** $t^2 - 3t - 18 = 0$ **21** $x^2 + x - 2 = 0$

22 $x^2 - 4x + 4 = 0$ **23** $m^2 - 10m + 25 = 0$ **24** $t^2 - 10t + 16 = 0$

25 $t^2 + 7t + 12 = 0$ **26** $k^2 - 3k - 18 = 0$ **27** $a^2 - 20a + 64 = 0$

HOMEWORK 12I

Give your answers either in rational form or as mixed numbers.

1   Solve the following equations.
     a $2x^2 + 5x + 2 = 0$ **b** $7x^2 + 8x + 1 = 0$ **c** $4x^2 + 3x - 7 = 0$
     d $6x^2 + 13x + 5 = 0$ **e** $6x^2 + 7x + 2 = 0$

2   Solve the following equations.
     a $x^2 - x = 6$ **b** $2x(4x + 7) = 3$ **c** $(x + 3)(x - 4) = 18$
     d $11x = 21 - 2x^2$ **e** $(2x + 3)(2x - 3) = 9x$

★**3**   **a**   Simplify $\dfrac{x^2 - 9}{3x - 9}$ **b**   Solve the equation $12x^2 - 25x + 12 = 0$

HOMEWORK 12J

Solve the following equations using the quadratic formula. Give your answers to 2 dp.

1 $3x^2 + x - 5 = 0$ **2** $2x^2 + 4x + 1 = 0$ **3** $x^2 - x - 7 = 0$

4 $3x^2 + x - 1 = 0$ **5** $3x^2 + 7x + 3 = 0$ **6** $2x^2 + 11x + 1 = 0$

7 $2x^2 + 5x + 1 = 0$ **8** $x^2 + 2x - 9 = 0$ **9** $x^2 + 2x - 6 = 0$

★**10**   Solve the equation $x^2 = 5x + 7$, giving your answers correct to 3 significant figures.

HOMEWORK 12K

1   Write an equivalent expression in the form $(x \pm a)^2 - b$.
     a $x^2 + 10x$ **b** $x^2 + 18x$ **c** $x^2 - 8x$ **d** $x^2 + 20x$ **e** $x^2 + 7x$

2   Write an equivalent expression in the form $( )^2 - b$.
     a $x^2 + 10x - 1$ **b** $x^2 + 18x - 5$ **c** $x^2 - 8x + 3$ **d** $x^2 - 5x - 1$

3   Solve the following equations by completing the square. Leave your answers in surd form where appropriate. The answers to Question **2** will help.
     a $x^2 + 10x - 1 = 0$ **b** $x^2 + 18x - 5 = 0$ **c** $x^2 - 8x + 3 = 0$
     d $x^2 + 20x + 7 = 0$ **e** $x^2 - 5x - 1 = 0$

4   Solve $x^2 + 8x - 3 = 0$ by completing the square. Give your answers to 2 dp.

★**5**   **a**   Write the equation $x^2 + 4x - 6$ in the form $(x + a)^2 - b$.
     b   Hence or otherwise, solve the equation $x^2 + 4x - 6 = 0$, leaving your answer in surd form.

Work out the discriminant $b^2 - 4ac$ of the following equations. In each case say how many solutions the equation has.

1 $3x^2 + 6x + 3 = 0$ **2** $2x^2 + 3x - 5 = 0$ **3** $2x^2 + 3x + 5 = 0$

4 $8x^2 + 3x - 2 = 0$ **5** $5x^2 + 4x + 1 = 0$ **6** $4x^2 + 4x + 1 = 0$

1 Solve the following equations. Give your answers in the form $a \pm \sqrt{b}$.

   a $x^2 - 6x - 4 = 0$ **b** $x^2 + 2x - 10 = 0$ **c** $x^2 + 6x - 8 = 0$

   d $x^2 + 4x - 6 = 0$ **e** $x^2 - 2x - 2 = 0$

2 Solve the following equations. Give your answers in surd form.

   a $2x^2 + 4x - 3 = 0$ **b** $3x^2 + 4x - 2 = 0$ **c** $2x^2 + 5x - 6 = 0$

   d $3x^2 - 5x - 6 = 0$ **e** $3x^2 + x - 5 = 0$

★3 $x + \dfrac{1}{x} = 3$

   a Show that this equation can be rearranged as $x^2 - 3x + 1 = 0$.

   b Solve this equation to find the values of x in surd form.

1 The sides of a right-angled triangle are $3x$, $(x + 1)$ and $(4x - 3)$. Find the actual dimensions of the triangle.

2 The length of a rectangle is 3 m more than its width. Its area is 130 m^2. Find the actual dimensions of the rectangle.

3 Solve the equation $x + \dfrac{2}{x} = 5$. Give your answers correct to 2 decimal places.

4 Solve the equation $3x + \dfrac{2}{x} = 7$.

5 The area of a triangle is 24 cm^2. The base is 8 cm longer than the height. Use this information to set up a quadratic equation. Solve the equation to find the length of the base.

6 On a journey of 210 km, the driver of a train calculates that if he were to increase his average speed by 10 km/h, he would take 30 minutes less. Find his average speed.

7 After a price increase for bananas of 25p per kilogram I can buy 2 kilograms less for £6 than I could last week. How much do bananas cost this week?

★8 Gareth took part in a 26 mile road race.

   a He ran the first 15 miles at an average speed of x mph. He ran the last 11 miles at an average speed of $(x - 2)$ mph. Write down an expression, in terms of x, for the time he took to complete the 26 mile race.

   b Gareth took four hours to complete the race. Using your answer to part **a**, form an equation in terms of x.

   c **i** Simplify your equation and show that it can be written as $2x^2 - 17x + 15 = 0$

      ii Solve the equation and obtain Gareth's average speed over the first 15 miles.

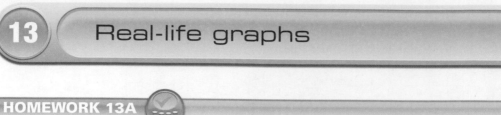

13 Real-life graphs

HOMEWORK 13A

1 Joe was travelling in his car to meet his girlfriend. He set off from home at 9.00 pm, and stopped on the way for a break. This distance–time graph illustrates his journey.

a At what time did he
   i stop for his break   **ii** set off after his break   **iii** get to his meeting place?
b At what average speed was he travelling
   i over the first hour   **ii** over the last hour   **iii** for the whole of his journey?

2 A taxi set off from Hellaby to pick up Jean. It then went on to pick up Jeans's parents. It then travelled further, dropping them all off at a shopping centre. The taxi then went on a further 10 km to pick up another party and took them back to Hellaby. This distance–time graph illustrates the journey.

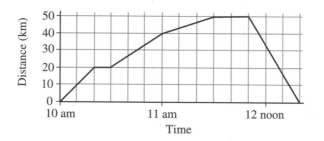

a How far from Hellaby did Jean's parents live?
b How far from Hellaby is the shopping centre?
c What was the average speed of the taxi while only Jean was in the taxi?
d What was the average speed of the taxi back to Hellaby?

3 Grandad took his grandchildren out for a trip. He set off at 1 pm and travelled, for half an hour, away from Sheffield at the average speed of 60 km/h. They stopped to look at the sea and have an ice cream. At two o'clock, they set off again, travelling for a quarter of an hour at a speed of 80 km/h. Here they stopped to play on the sand for half an hour. Grandad then drove the grandchildren back home, at an average speed of 50 km/h. Draw a travel graph to illustrate this story. Use a horizontal axis to represent time from 1 pm to 5 pm, and a vertical scale from 0 km to 50 km.

1 Calculate the gradient of each line.

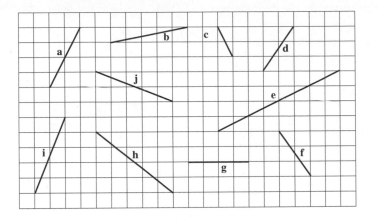

2 Calculate the average speed of the journey represented by each line in the following diagrams. The gradient of each line is the speed.

3 This is a conversion graph between ounces and grams.
a Calculate the gradient of the line.
b Use the graph to find the number of grams equivalent to 1 ounce.

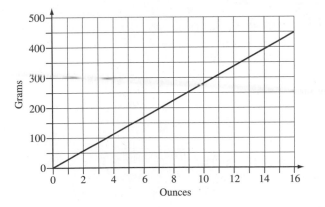

1 The diagram shows the velocity of
a car over 10 seconds.
Calculate the acceleration
a over the first 2 seconds
b after 6 seconds.

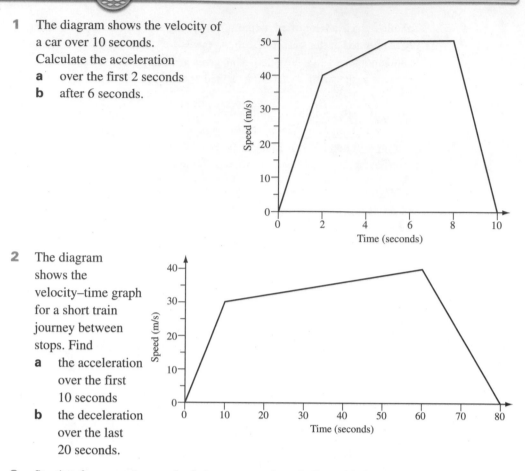

2 The diagram
shows the
velocity–time graph
for a short train
journey between
stops. Find
a the acceleration
over the first
10 seconds
b the deceleration
over the last
20 seconds.

3 Starting from rest (zero velocity), a car travels as indicated below.
- Accelerates at a constant rate over 10 seconds to reach 20 m/s.
- Keeps this velocity for 30 seconds.
- Accelerates over the next 10 seconds to reach 30 m/s.
- Steadily slows down to reach rest (zero velocity) over the next 20 seconds.
a Draw the velocity–time graph.
b Calculate the deceleration over the last 20 seconds.

★**4** This graph represents the journey
of a train.
a What was the average speed of
the train from A to B?
b How long did the train wait
at B?
c Another train starts from C at
11 00 and travels non-stop to A
at an average speed of 60 mph.
Draw the graph of its journey on
a copy of the graph.
d Write down how far from A the
trains were when they passed
each other.

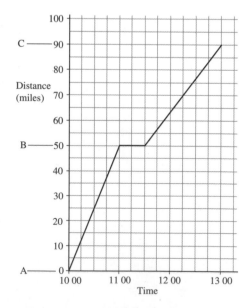

1   The following is a simplified model of how a savings scheme would work.
    £100 is invested at the start of a year. At the end of the first year 7% interest is added to
    this and another £100 is invested. This gives a total of £207 at the start of the second year.
    At the end of the second year 7% is added and another £100 is invested. This continues
    for another 10 years.
    a   Calculate the amount of money in the scheme at the start of each year.
    b   Draw a graph of money in scheme against year. (First point will be (0, 100), second
        point will be (2, 207). Take the horizontal axis as 'Years' from 0 to 10. Take the
        vertical axis as 'Savings' from £0 to £1500.)

2   Flexible loans are loans where the amount paid back can vary. People usually take these
    out when they cannot pay a lot back at first but know that their income will increase so
    that they can pay a lot more back as time goes on. The Jones take out a £1000 loan at 8%
    interest. They pay back £50 after the first year, £75 after the second year, £100 after the
    third year and so on.
    This is the calculation of what they owe for the first 2 years.
        First year interest £1000 × 1.08 = £1080.
        Amount owed at end of first year £1080 – £50 = £1030 owed.
        Second year interest £1030 × 1.08 = £1112.40.
        Amount owed at end of second year £1112.40 – 75 = £1037.40.
    a   Continue the calculation until the debt is paid off.
    b   Draw a graph of time (years) against amount owed.

3   Draw a graph of the depth of water in each of these containers as it is filled steadily.

a   b   c   d

★4 a   Each of the four graphs below represents **one** of the following **five** situations.
        Situation A   The first 4 seconds of a sprinter's 100 metre race.
        Situation B   A train travelling at a constant 15 m/s taking 4 seconds to pass
                           through a tunnel.
        Situation C   A ball thrown vertically upwards and caught by the thrower
                           4 seconds later.
        Situation D   A ball rolling from rest down a smooth slope for 4 seconds.
        Situation E   A lift setting off from one floor and stopping 4 seconds later at the
                           next floor.

1

2

3

4

Match each graph with one of the five situations.

b One of the situations A, B, C, D or E does not match any of the four graphs drawn in part **a**. Sketch the speed–time graph for this situation.

14 Similarity

HOMEWORK 14A

1 These diagrams are drawn to scale. What is the scale factor of the enlargement in each case?

2 a Explain why these two shapes are similar.
  b Give the ratio of the sides.
  c Which angle corresponds to angle C?
  d Which side corresponds to side QP?

3 In the diagrams below, find the lengths of the sides marked x. Each pair of shapes is similar but not drawn to scale.

a

b

1   In each of the cases below, state a pair of similar triangles and find the length marked x.
    Separate the similar triangles if it makes it easier for you.

    a   **b**

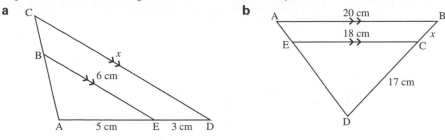

2   In the diagrams below, find the lengths of the sides marked x and y..

    a   **b**

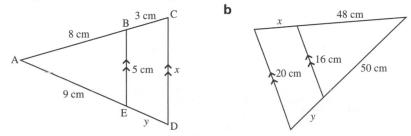

3   Find the height of a lamppost which casts a shadow of 2.1 metres when at the same time a
    man of height 158 cm casts a shadow of 90 cm.

4   Amy is 115 cm tall, she notices that when her mum, who is 175 cm tall, stands $2\frac{1}{2}$ metres
    away from her she looks as tall as the Cutlers Hall. Amy is standing 30 metres away from
    the Cutlers Hall when she notices this. How high is the Cutlers Hall?

Find the lengths x and y in the diagrams below.

1 The length ratio between two similar solids is 3 : 7.
   a What is the area ratio between the solids?
   b What is the volume ratio between the solids?

2 Copy and complete this table.

Linear scale factor	Linear ratio	Linear fraction	Area scale factor	Volume scale factor
4	1 : 4	$\frac{4}{1}$		
$\frac{1}{2}$				
	10 : 1			
			36	
				125

3 A shape has an area of 20 cm^2. What is the area of a similar shape whose lengths are four times the corresponding lengths of the first shape.

4 A brick has a volume of 400 cm^3. What would be the volume of a similar brick whose lengths are
   a three times the corresponding lengths of the first brick
   b five times the corresponding lengths of the first brick?

5 A can of paint, 12 cm high, holds five litres of paint. How much paint would go into a similar can which is 30 cm high?

6 A model statue is 15 cm high and has a volume of 450 cm^3. The real statue is 4.5 m high. What is the volume of the real statue? Give your answer in m^3.

7 A triangle has sides of 5, 12 and 13 cm. Its area is 30 cm^2. How long are the sides of a similar triangle that has an area of 270 cm^2?

8 A cuboid with one side of r cm has a volume of x cm^3. What is the volume of a similar cuboid with one side of $3r$ cm?

9 What is **a** the linear scale factor and **b** the volume scale factor that corresponds to an area scale factor of $4a^2$

★**10** A model motorbike is similar to the real bike in every detail. The scale is 1 : 10.
   a The real bike's wheels have a diameter of 50 cm. What is the diameter of the model bike's wheels.
   b The petrol tank on the real bike holds 12 litres. How much will the petrol tank on the model bike hold?
   c The seat on the model bike took 20 cm^2 of leather to cover it. How much leather will be needed to cover the seat on the real bike?

HOMEWORK 14E

1 A firm produces three sizes of paper. Their areas are 600 cm^2, 900 cm^2 and 1200 cm^2. The dimensions of the smaller size are 20 cm by 30 cm. Calculate the dimensions of the other two sizes of paper.

2 A firm makes similar bottles in three different sizes: small, medium and large. The volumes are
   small   330 cm^3 medium   1000 cm^3 large   2000 cm^3

a The medium bottle is 20 cm high. Find the heights of the other two bottles.

b The labels on the bottles are also similar. The large bottle has a label with an area of 100 cm². Find the areas of the labels on the other two bottles.

3 It takes 6 litres of paint to cover a wall with an area of 12 square metres. How large an area would 24 litres of paint cover?

4 It takes 30 minutes for 3 towels to dry on a washing line. How long would it take 6 similar towels to dry ?

5 It takes 1 kg of grass seed to cover a lawn that is 20 metres long. How much seed will be needed to cover a similar shaped lawn that is 10 metres long.

6 A model yacht has a mast 40 cm high. The real yacht has a mast 4 metres high.

a The sail on the model yacht has an area of 600 cm². What is the area of the real sail. Answer in m².

b The real yacht has a hull volume of 20 m³. What is the hull volume of the model yacht? Answer in cm³.

7 A triangle is enlarged as shown from the origin as centre.
The point A(2, 1) is transformed to A′(6, 3).
The area of the original triangle is 4 cm².
What is the area of the transformed triangle?

★8 The ratio of the height of P to the height of Q is 5 : 4. The volume of P is 150 cm³. Calculate the volume of Q.

Not to scale

15 Trigonometry

HOMEWORK 15A

1 A child's toy consists of a ball that fits into a cone.
The ball has a radius of 3 cm. The base angle of the cone is 38°.
Find

a AB   **b** OB   **c** AC

2 From the top of a building 24 metres high the angle of depression of both ends of a tennis court are 43° and 28° respectively.

a Calculate the length of the court.

b The net is half way along the court and is 1 metre high. What is the angle of depression of the top of the net from the building?

3 A ship leaves a port A and travels for 80 km on a bearing of 300° to a point B. It then turns and travels for 40 km on a bearing of 030° to a point C. Calculate
a how far west of A point C is
b how far north of A point C is
c the bearing of A from C
d the direct distance of A from C.

★**4** A tower, CD, is at the top of a hill, BC. Martin measures the distance AC as 70 m and the angles of elevation of the top and bottom of the tower as 25° and 42° respectively. Calculate
a angle CAD
b length AB
c length CB
d height of tower, CD.

HOMEWORK 15B

1 The diagram shows a pyramid. The base is a square ABCD, 16 cm by 16 cm. The length of each sloping edge is 25 cm. The apex, V, is over the centre of the base. Calculate
a the size of the angle VAC
b the height of the pyramid
c the volume of the pyramid
d the size of the angle between the face VAD and the base ABCD.

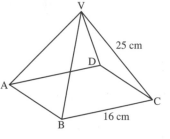

2 In the given cuboid, find
a angle AGE
b angle BMA
(M is the mid-point of GH)

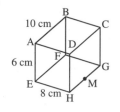

3 The diagram shows a wedge. Find
a CD
b angle CAD
c angle CAE
The point M is the mid-point of AB. Calculate
d the distance DM
e the angle of elevation of M from D.

★**4** A tetrahedron VPQR stands on a prism FGHPQR. The cross-section PQR is an equilateral triangle of side 8 cm. VP = VQ = VR = 10 cm. PF = QG = RH = 15 cm. M is the mid-point of QR.
a **i** Use triangle PQR to find the length of PM.
   ii Use triangle VQR to find the length of VM.
b Find the size of angle VPM.
c Find the height of V above the base FGH. Give your answer to an appropriate degree of accuracy.

State the two angles between 0° and 360° for each of these sine values.

1 0.4   **2** 0.45   **3** 0.65   **4** 0.27

5 0.453   **6** −0.4   **7** −0.15   **8** −0.52

9 Solve the equation $2 \sin x = 1$ for $0° \leqslant x \leqslant 360°$.

10 $\sin 40° = 0.643$. Write down the sine values of these angles.

     i 140°   **ii** 320°   **iii** 400°   **iv** 580°

★**11** Solve the equation $3 \sin x = -2$ for $0° \leqslant x \leqslant 360°$.

State the two angles between 0° and 360° for each of these cosine values.

1 0.7   **2** 0.38   **3** 0.617   **4** 0.376

5 0.085   **6** −0.6   **7** −0.45   **8** −0.223

9 Solve the equation $3 \cos x = -1$ for $0° \leqslant x \leqslant 360°$.

10 $\cos 50° = 0.643$. Write down the cosine values of these angles.

     i 130°   **ii** 310°   **iii** 410°   **iv** 590°.

★**11** Solve the equation $6 \cos x = -1$ for $0° \leqslant x \leqslant 360°$.

1 Write down the sine of each of these angles.

     a 27°   **b** 153°   **c** 207°   **d** 333°

2 Write down the cosine of each of these angles.

     a 69°   **b** 111°   **c** 249°   **d** 291°

3 What do you notice about the answers to Questions **1** and **2**?

4 Find four values between 0° and 360° such that

     a $\sin x = \pm 0.4$ **b** $\cos x = \pm 0.5$

5 Solve   **a** $\sin x + 1 = 2$ for $0° \leqslant x \leqslant 360°$ **b** $2 + 3 \cos x = 1$ for $0° \leqslant x \leqslant 360°$

★**6** Find two values of x between 0° and 360° such that $\sin x = \cos 320°$.

State the angles between 0° and 360° for each of these tangent values.

1 0.528   **2** 0.8   **3** 1.35   **4** 3.24

5 −2.55   **6** −0.158   **7** −0.786   **8** −1.999

9 Solve the equation $2 \tan x = -3$ for $0° \leqslant x \leqslant 360°$

10 $\tan 64° = 2.05$. Write down the tangent values of these angles.

     i 116°   **ii** 296°   **iii** 424°   **iv** 604°

★**11** Solve the equation $2 \tan x - 5 = -1$ for $0° \leqslant x \leqslant 360°$.

1 Find the length x in each of these triangles

a

b

2 Find the angle x in each of these triangles

a

b

3 In triangle ABC, the angle at A is 40°, the side AB is 10 cm and the side BC is 7 cm. Find the two possible values of the angle at C.

4 In triangle ABC, the angle at A is 58°, the side AB is 20 cm and the side BC is 18 cm. Find the two possible values of the side AC.

5 To calculate the length of a submarine Mervyn stands on a cliff 60 m high and measures the angle of depression of both ends of the boat. The information is shown in the diagram.

    a Find the value of the angle DAB.

    b Use trigonometry to calculate the length AB.

    c Use the sine rule to find the length BC.

6 Use the information on this sketch to calculate the width, w, of the river.

★7 A surveyor wishes to measure the height of a chimney. Measuring the angle of elevation, she finds that the angle increases from 28° to 37° after walking 30 metres towards the chimney. What is the height of the chimney?

1 Find the length x in each of these triangles.

a

b

2   Find the angle x in each of these triangles.

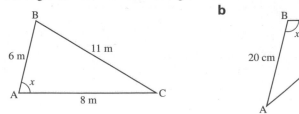

a

B

6 m   11 m

A x C

8 m

b

B   18 cm   C

x

20 cm   32 cm

A

3   A quadrilateral ABCD has AD = 8 cm, DC = 10 cm, AB = 12 cm and BC = 15 cm. Angle ADC = 112°. Calculate angle ABC.

4   The three sides of a triangle are given as $2a$, $3a$ and $5a$. Calculate the smallest angle in the triangle.

5   The diagram shows a trapezium ABCD.
AB = 6 cm, AD = 8 cm, CB = 12 cm and angle DAB = 115°. Calculate
  a   length DB   **b**   angle DBA
  c   angle DBC   **d**   length DC
  e   area of the trapezium.

D   8 cm   A

115°   6 cm

C   12 cm   B

 ★6   A port, B, is 20 km north east of another port, A. A lighthouse, L, is 5 km from B on a bearing of 260° from B. Calculate
  a   the distance AL   **b**   the bearing of L from A to the nearest degree.

HOMEWORK 15I

1   Find the length or angle x in each of these triangles.

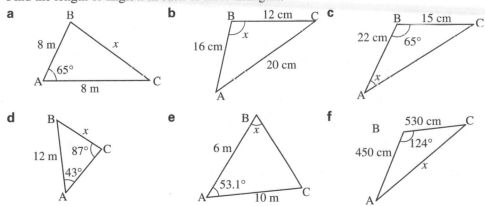

a

B

8 m x

A   65°   C

8 m

b

B   12 cm   C

x

16 cm   20 cm

A

c

B   15 cm   C

22 cm   65°

A x

d

B

x

12 m   87°   C

43°

A

e

B

x

6 m   C

A   53.1°   10 m

f

B   530 cm   C

450 cm   124°

A x

2   The hands of a clock have lengths 10 cm and 7 cm. Find the distance between the tips of the hands at 5 O'clock.

3   In the quadrilateral ABCD, find
  a   angle ABC
  b   the length of AC.

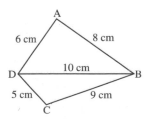

A

6 cm   8 cm

D   10 cm   B

5 cm   9 cm

C

 ★4   In a triangle, ABC, AC = 7.6 cm, angle BAC = 35°, angle ACB = 65°. The length of AB is x cm. Calculate the value of x.

1 The sine of angle x is $\frac{3}{4}$.

Work out the cosine of angle x.

3 cm   4 cm x

2 The cosine of angle x is $\dfrac{3}{\sqrt{18}}$.

Work out the value of angle x.

√18 cm x 3 cm

3 Calculate the exact value of the area of an equilateral triangle of side a cm.

4 Work out the exact value of the area of a right-angled isosceles triangle whose hypotenuse is 10 cm.

★**5** A right-angled triangle has short sides of length √6 cm and √10 cm.

    a Calculate the length of the hypotenuse.

    b Write down the values of sin x and cos x.

    c Show clearly that $(\sin x)^2 + (\cos x)^2 = 1$.

√6   √10 x

1 Find the area of each of the following triangles.

    a Triangle ABC where BC = 8 cm, AC = 10 cm and angle ACB = 69°.

    b Triangle ABC where angle BAC = 112°, AC = 3 cm and AB = 7 cm.

2 The area of triangle ABC is 27 cm². If BC = 12 cm and angle BCA = 98°, find AC.

3 In a quadrilateral ABCD, DC = 3 cm, BD = 8 cm, angle BAD = 43°, angle ABD = 52° and angle BDC = 72°. Calculate the area of the quadrilateral.

4 The area of triangle LMN is 85 cm², LM = 10 cm and MN = 25 cm. Calculate

    a angle LMN   **b** angle MNL.

 5 A board is in the shape of a triangle with sides 30 cm, 40 cm and 60 cm. Find its area.

 ★**6** In the triangle ABC, angle B is **obtuse**, ∠BAC = 32°, AC = 10 cm, BC = 6 cm. Calculate the area of the triangle ABC.

B   6 cm   A   32°   10 cm   C

Draw the graph for each of the equations given.

Follow these hints.

- Use the highest and smallest values of x given as your range.
- When the first part of the function is a division, pick x-values that divide exactly to avoid fractions.
- Always label your graphs. This is particularly important when you are drawing two graphs on the same set of axes.
- Create a table of values. You will often have to complete these in your examinations.

1 Draw the graph of $y = 2x + 3$ for x-values from 0 to 5 ($0 \leqslant x \leqslant 5$).

2 Draw the graph of $y = 3x - 1$ ($0 \leqslant x \leqslant 5$)

3 Draw the graph of $y = \dfrac{x}{2} - 2$ ($0 \leqslant x \leqslant 12$)

4 Draw the graph of $y = 2x + 1$ ($-2 \leqslant x \leqslant 2$)

5 Draw the graph of $y = \dfrac{x}{2} + 5$ ($-6 \leqslant x \leqslant 6$)

6 **a** On the same set of axes, draw the graphs of
$y = 3x - 1$ and $y = 2x + 3$ ($0 \leqslant x \leqslant 5$)
   b Where do the two graphs cross?

7 **a** On the same axes, draw the graphs of
$y = 4x - 3$ and $y = 3x + 2$ ($0 \leqslant x \leqslant 6$)
   b Where do the two graphs cross?

8 **a** On the same axes, draw the graphs of
$y = \dfrac{x}{2} + 1$ and $y = \dfrac{x}{3} + 2$ ($0 \leqslant x \leqslant 12$)
   b Where do the two graphs cross?

9 **a** On the same axes, draw the graphs of
$y = 2x + 3$ and $y = 2x - 1$ ($0 \leqslant x \leqslant 4$)
   b Do the graphs cross? If not, why not?

10 **a** Copy and complete the table to draw the graph of

x	0	1	2	3	4	5	6
y							

$x + y = 6$ ($0 \leqslant x \leqslant 6$)
   b Now draw the graph of $x + y = 3$.

1   Find the gradient of each of these lines.

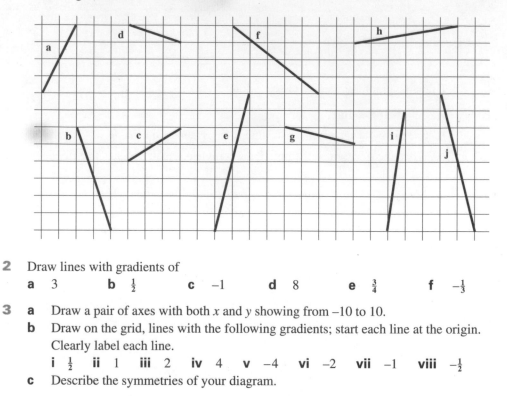

2   Draw lines with gradients of
    a 3   **b** $\frac{1}{2}$ **c** -1 **d** 8   **e** $\frac{3}{4}$ **f** $-\frac{1}{3}$

3   **a**   Draw a pair of axes with both x and y showing from -10 to 10.
    b   Draw on the grid, lines with the following gradients; start each line at the origin.
            Clearly label each line.
            i $\frac{1}{2}$ **ii** 1   **iii** 2   **iv** 4   **v** -4 **vi** -2 **vii** -1 **viii** $-\frac{1}{2}$
    c   Describe the symmetries of your diagram.

1   Draw these lines using the gradient-intercept method. Use the same grid, taking both x
    and y from -10 to 10. If the grid gets too 'crowded', draw another one.
    a $y = 2x + 4$ **b** $y = 3x - 2$ **c** $y = \frac{1}{2}x + 1$ **d** $y = x + 5$
    e $y = 4x - 1$ **f** $y = 2x - 5$ **g** $y = \frac{1}{4}x - 1$ **h** $y = x - 1$
    i $y = 6x - 2$ **j** $y = x + 3$ **k** $y = \frac{3}{4}x - 2$ **l** $y = 3x - 4$

    For the next questions, use grids showing x, from -6 to 6, and y, from -8 to 8.

2   **a**   Using the gradient-intercept method, draw the following lines on the same grid.
            i $y = 3x + 2$ **ii** $y = 2x - 1$
    b   Where do the lines cross?

3   **a**   Using the gradient-intercept method, d.   he following lines on the same grid.
            i $y = x + 2$ **ii** $y = 5x$
    b   Where do the lines cross?

1   Draw these lines using the cover-up method. Use the same grid, taking x from -10 to 10
    and y from -10 to 10. If the grid gets too 'crowded', draw another.
    a $2x + 3y = 6$ **b** $3x + 4y = 12$ **c** $5x - 4y = 20$ **d** $x + y = 8$
    e $2x - 3y = 18$ **f** $x - y = 6$ **g** $3x - 5y = 15$ **h** $3x - 2y = 12$
    i $5x + 4y = 30$ **j** $x + y = -1$ **k** $x + y = 5$ **l** $x - y = -6$

2 a Using the cover-up method, draw the following lines on the same grid.

    i $x + 2y = 4$ **ii** $2x - y = 2$

  b Where do the lines cross?

3 Using the cover-up method, draw the following lines on the same grid.

    $x + 2y = 6$ $2x - y = 2$

  Where do the lines cross?

HOMEWORK 16E

1 Give the equation of each of these lines.

a   **b**   **c**

2 In each of these grids, there are two lines.

a   **b**   **c**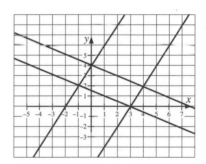

  i Find the equation of each line.

  ii Describe any symmetries you see about the two lines.

3 The diagram shows four lines crossing to create a rectangle. Write down the equation of each of the four lines.

HOMEWORK 16F

1 This graph illustrates the charges made by an electricity company.

  a Calculate the standing charge, this is the amount paid before any electricity is used.

  b What is the gradient of the line?

  c From your answers to **a** and **b** write down the rule to calculate the total charge for electricity.

2 This graph illustrates the charges made by a gas company.

   a Calculate the standing charge.

   b What is the gradient of the line?

   c From your answers to **a** and **b** write down the rule to calculate the total charge for gas.

★3 This graph illustrates the charges made by a phone company.

   a Calculate the standing charge.

   b What is the gradient of the line?

   c From your answers to **a** and **b** write down the rule to calculate the total charge for using this phone company.

HOMEWORK 16G

By drawing their graphs, find the solution of each of these pairs of simultaneous equations.

1 $x + 4y = 1$
   $x - y = 6$

2 $y = 2x + 1$
   $3x + 2y = 23$

3 $y = 2x + 5$
   $y = x + 4$

4 $y = x$
   $x - y = 4$

5 $y + 10 = 2x$
   $5x + y = 18$

6 $y = 5x - 1$
   $y = 3x + 2$

7 $y = x + 11$
   $x + y = 5$

8 $y - 3x = 8$
   $y = x + 6$

9 $y = -x$
   $y = 4x + 15$

10 $3x + 2y = 2$
   $y = -2x$

11 $y = 3x - 4$
   $y + x = 6$

12 $y = 3x - 12$
   $x + y = 2$

HOMEWORK 16H

1 Write down the equation of the line perpendicular to each of the following lines and which passes through the same point on the y-axis.

   a $y = 2x - 3$
   b $y = -4x + 3$
   c $y = \frac{1}{2}x - 5$
   d $y = -\frac{1}{4}x - 3$

2 Write down the equations of these lines.

   a parallel to $y = 3x - 2$ and passes through $(0, 4)$

   b parallel to $y = \frac{1}{4}x + 3$ and passes through $(0, -1)$

   c parallel to $y = -x + 3$ and passes through $(0, 2)$

3 Find the equation of the line that passes through the mid-point of AB, and is perpendicular to AB, where A is $(1,4)$ and B is $(5,2)$.

More graphs and equations

1 **a** Copy and complete the table for the graph of $y = 2x^2$ for $-3 \leqslant x \leqslant 3$.

x	-3	-2	-1	0	1	2	3
$y = 2x^2$	18		2			8	

b Use your graph to find the value of y when $x = -1.4$.

c Use your graph to find the values of x that give a y-value of 10.

2 **a** Copy and complete the table for the graph of $y = x^2 + 3$ for $-5 \leqslant x \leqslant 5$.

x	-5	-4	-3	-2	-1	0	1	2	3	4	5
$y = x^2 + 3$	28		12					7			28

b Use your graph to find the value of y when $x = 2.5$.

c Use your graph to find the values of x that give a y-value of 10.

★**3** **a** Copy and complete the table for the graph of $y = x^2 - 3x + 2$ for $-3 \leqslant x \leqslant 4$.

x	-3	-2	-1	0	1	2	3	4
$y = x^2 - 3x + 2$	20			2			2	

b Use your graph to find the value of y when $x = -1.5$.

c Use your graph to find the values of x that give a y-value of 2.5.

1 **a** Copy and complete the table to draw the graph of $y = x^2 - 3x + 2$ for $-1 \leqslant x \leqslant 5$.

x	-1	0	1	2	3	4	5
$y = x^2 - 3x + 2$	6	2			1		

b Use your graph to find the roots of the equation $x^2 - 3x + 2 = 0$.

2 **a** Copy and complete the table to draw the graph of $y = x^2 - 5x + 4$ for $-1 \leqslant x \leqslant 6$.

x	-1	0	1	2	3	4	5	6
$y = x^2 - 5x + 4$	10	4				0		

b Use your graph to find the roots of the equation $x^2 - 5x + 4 = 0$.

3 **a** Copy and complete the table to draw the graph of $y = x^2 + 4x - 6$ for $-5 \leqslant x \leqslant 2$.

x	-5	-4	-3	-2	-1	0	1	2
$y = x^2 + 4x - 6$	-1							6

b Use your graph to find the roots of the equation $x^2 + 4x - 6 = 0$.

1 **a** Complete the table to draw the graph of $y = \dfrac{12}{x}$ for $-12 \leqslant x \leqslant 12$.

x	−12	−6	−4	−3	−2	−1	1	2	3	4	6	12
$y = \dfrac{12}{x}$	−1			−4					4			1

b Use your graph to find
  i the y-value when $x = 1.5$ **ii** the x-value when $y = 5.5$.

★**2** **a** Complete the table to draw the graph of $y = \dfrac{8}{x}$ for $-8 \leqslant x \leqslant 8$.

x	−8	−5	−4	−2	−1	2	4	5	8
$y = \dfrac{8}{x}$									

b Use your graph to find
  i the y-value when $x = 3.5$ **ii** the x-value when $y = 5$.

3 **a** Complete the table to draw the graph of $y = \dfrac{50}{x}$ for $0 \leqslant x \leqslant 50$.

x	1	2	5	10	25	50
$y = \dfrac{50}{x}$						

b On the same axes, draw the line $y = x + 30$.
c Use your graph to find the x-value of the point where the graphs cross.

1 **a** Complete the table to draw the graph of $y = x^3 + 1$ for $-3 \leqslant x \leqslant 3$.

x	−3	−2	−1	0	1	2	3
$y = x^3 + 1$	−26			1			28

b Use your graph to find the y-value for an x-value of 1.2.

★**2** **a** Complete the table to draw the graph of $y = x^3 + 2x$ for $-2 \leqslant x \leqslant 3$.

x	−2	−1	0	1	2	3
$y = x^3 + 2x$	−12		0		12	

b Use your graph to find the y-value for a x-value of 2.5.

3 **a** Draw the graph of $y = x^3 - x^2$ for $-3 \leqslant x \leqslant 3$.
b Use your graph to find the y-value for an x-value of 1.8.

1 a Complete the table below for $y = 2^x$ for values of x from –3 to +4. (Values are rounded to 2 dp.)

x	–3	–2	–1	0	1	2	3	4
$y = 2^x$	0.1	0.3			2	4		

b Plot the graph of $y = 2^x$ for $-3 \leqslant x \leqslant 4$ (Take y-axis from 0 to 20)
c Use your graph to estimate the value of y when $x = 2.5$.
d Use your graph to estimate the value of x when $y = 0.75$.

2 a Complete the table below for $y = (\frac{1}{3})^x$ for values of x from –3 to +3 (Values are rounded to 2 dp.)

x	–3	–2	–1	0	1	2	3
$y = (\frac{1}{3})^x$	27			1			0.04

b Plot the graph of $y = (\frac{1}{3})^x$ for $-3 \leqslant x \leqslant 3$ (Take y-axis from 0 to 30)
c Use your graph to estimate the value of y when $x = 2.5$.
b Use your graph to estimate the value of x when $y = 0.75$.

3 Granny has two nephews, Alf and Bert. She writes a will leaving Alf £1000 in the first year after her death. £2000 in the second year after her death, £3000 the next year and so on for 20 years. She leaves Bert £1 the first year, £2 the second year, £4 the next year and so on.
a Show that the formula $500n(n + 1)$ gives the total mount that Alf gets after n years
b Show that the formula $2^n - 1$ gives the total amount that Bert gets after n years.
c Complete the table for the total amount of money that Bert gets.

Year	2	4	6	8	10	12	14	16	18	20
Total	3	15	63							

d Draw a graph of both nephews total over 20 years. Take the x-axis from 0 to 20 years and the y-axis from £0 to £110 000.
e Which nephew gets the better deal?

1 Given that $\sin 55° = 0.819$, find another angle between 0° and 360° that also has a sine of 0.819.

2 Given that $\sin 225° = -0.707$, find another angle between 0° and 360° that also has a sine of –0.707.

3 Given that $\cos 27° = 0.891$, find another angle between 0° and 360° that also has a cosine of 0.891.

4 Given that $\cos 123° = –0.545$, find another angle between 0° and 360° that also has a cosine of –0.545.

5 Given that $\sin 60° = 0.866$, find two angles between 0° and 360° that have a sine of –0.866.

6 Given that $\cos 30° = 0.866$, find two angles between 0° and 360° that have a cosine of –0.866.

7 Given that $\cos 38° = 0.788$
a write down an angle between 0° and 360° that has a sine of 0.788
b find two angles between 0° and 360° that have a cosine of –0.788
c find two angles between 0° and 360° that have a sine of –0.788.

1 Below is the graph of $y = x^2 - 2x - 4$.
Use this graph to solve
  a $x^2 - 2x - 4 = 0$
  b $x^2 - 2x - 4 = 4$
  c $x^2 - 2x - 3 = 0$

2 Below are the graphs of $y = x^2 - 3x + 1$
and $y = x - 1$. Use these graphs to solve
  a $x^2 - 3x + 1 = 0$
  b $x^2 - 4x + 2 = 0$
  c   What straight-line graph will you need
to draw to solve $x^2 - 4x + 3 = 0$?
Draw this line and write down the two
solutions to $x^2 - 4x + 3 = 0$.

3 Draw the graph of $y = x^3 - 2x + 3$.
  a   Use the graph to solve   **i** $x^3 - 2x + 3 = 0$ **ii** $x^3 - 2x = 0$
  b   What straight-line graph will you need to draw to solve $x^3 - 3x + 2 = 0$?
     Draw this line and solve $x^3 - 3x + 2 = 0$.

4 The graph of $y = x^3 - 4x - 1$ is shown on the right.
  a   Use the graph to solve
     i $x^3 - 4x - 1 = 0$
     ii $x^3 - 4x + 2 = 0$
  b   By drawing an appropriate straight line solve the
     equation $x^3 - 5x - 1 = 0$.

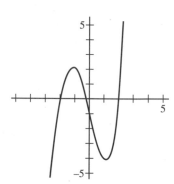

★5 The graph of $y = x^3 - 4x$ is shown.

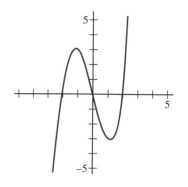

  a   Use the graph to find the two positive
     solutions to $x^3 - 4x = -2$.
  b   By drawing an appropriate straight line
     use the graph to solve $x^3 - 3x + 1 = 0$.

1 The table shows the estimated number of visits to the cinema in Sheffield.

Year	1970	1975	1980	1985	1990	1995	2000	2005
No. of visits (thousands)	280	110	180	330	510	620	750	810

    a Draw a line graph for this data.

    b From your graph estimate the number of visits to the cinema in Sheffield in 1998.

    c In which 5 year period did the number of visits increase the most?

    d Explain the trend in the number of visits. What reasons can you give to explain this trend?

1 The weights of 15 tomatoes are measured:

       62 g, 58 g, 60 g, 48 g, 55 g

       53 g, 62 g, 67 g, 57 g, 54 g

       60 g, 57 g, 62 g, 47 g, 67 g

    a Show the results in an ordered stem-and-leaf diagram, using this key

       key: 6|3 represents 63 g

    b What was the greatest weight recorded?

    c What was the most common weight measured?

    d What is the difference between the largest and smallest weights measured?

2 A group of friends compare how many new DVDs they had watched during the Christmas break.

       11, 19, 20, 4, 18, 22, 4, 8, 21, 14, 18, 23, 8, 8, 17, 23

    a Show the results in an ordered stem-and-leaf diagram, using this key

       key: 1|3 represents 13 new DVDs watched

    b What was the highest number of new DVDs that any of the group watched?

    c What was the most common number of new DVDs watched in the break?

1 The table shows the heights and weights of twelve students in a class.

    a Plot the data on a scatter diagram.

    b Draw the line of best fit.

    c Jayne was absent from the class, but they knew she was 132 cm tall. Use the line of best fit to estimate her weight.

    d A new girl joined the class who weighed 55 kg. What height would you expect her to be?

Student	Weight (kg)	Height (cm)
Ann	51	123
Bridie	58	125
Ciri	57.5	127
Di	62	128
Emma	59.5	129
Flo	65	129
Gill	65	133
Hanna	65.5	135
Ivy	71	137
Joy	75.5	140
Keri	70	143
Laura	78	145

★2 The table shows the marks for ten pupils in their mathematics and music examinations.

    a Plot the data on a scatter diagram. Take the x-axis for the mathematics scores and mark it from 20 to 100. Take the y-axis for the music scores and mark it from 20 to 100.

    b Draw the line of best fit.

    c One of the pupils was ill when they took the music examination. Which pupil was it most likely to be?

    d Another pupil, Kris, was absent for the music examination but scored 45 in mathematics, what mark would you expect him to have got in music?

Pupil	Maths	Music
Alex	52	50
Ben	42	52
Chris	65	60
Don	60	59
Ellie	77	61
Fan	83	74
Gary	78	64
Hazel	87	68
Irene	29	26
Jez	53	45

    e Another pupil, Lex, was absent for the mathematics examination but scored 78 in music, what mark would you expect him to have got in mathematics?

HOMEWORK 18D

1 An army squad were all sent on a one mile run. Their coach recorded the times they actually took. This table shows the results.

    a Copy the table and complete a cumulative frequency column.

    b Draw a cumulative frequency diagram.

    c Use your diagram to estimate the median time and the interquartile range.

Time (seconds)	Number of players
$200 < x \leqslant 240$	3
$240 < x \leqslant 260$	7
$260 < x \leqslant 280$	12
$280 < x \leqslant 300$	23
$300 < x \leqslant 320$	7
$320 < x \leqslant 340$	5
$340 < x \leqslant 360$	5

★2 A company had 360 web pages. They recorded how many times they were visited on one day.

    a Copy the table and complete a cumulative frequency column.

    b Draw a cumulative frequency diagram.

    c Use your diagram to estimate the median use of the web pages and the interquartile range.

    d Pages with less than 60 visitors are going to be rewritten. About how many pages would need to be rewritten?

Number of visits	Number of pages
$0 < x \leqslant 50$	6
$50 < x \leqslant 100$	9
$100 < x \leqslant 150$	15
$150 < x \leqslant 200$	25
$200 < x \leqslant 250$	31
$250 < x \leqslant 300$	37
$300 < x \leqslant 350$	32
$350 < x \leqslant 400$	17
$400 < x \leqslant 450$	5

1 The box plot below shows the number of peas in pods grown by a prize-winning gardener.

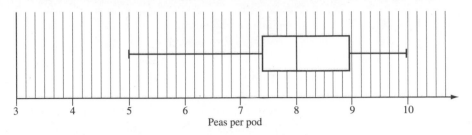

Peas per pod

A young gardener also grew some peas. These are the results for the number of peas per pod. Smallest number 3, Lower quartile 4.75, Median 5.5, Upper quartile 6.25, Highest number 9.

a Copy the diagram and draw a box plot for the young gardener.

b Comment on the differences between the two distributions.

2 The box plot shows the monthly salaries of the men in a computer firm.

Monthly salary (£s)

The data for the women in the company is Smallest 600, Lower quartile 1300, Median 1600, Upper Quartile 2000, Largest 2400.

a Copy the diagram and draw a box plot for the women's salaries.

b Comment on the differences between the two distributions.

3 The box plots for the hours of life of two brands of batteries are shown below.

Hours of life

a Comment on the differences in the two distributions.

b Mushtaq wants to get some batteries for his palm top. Which brand would you recommend and why?

4 The following table shows some data on the times of telephone calls to two operators at a mobile phone helpline.

	Lowest time	Lowest Quartile	Medium time	Upper Quartile	Highest time
Jack	1 m 10 s	2 m 20 s	3 m 30 s	4 m 50 s	7 m 10 s
Jill	40 s	2 m 20 s	5 m 10 s	7 m 30 s	10 m 45 s

a Draw box plots to compare both sets of data.

b Comment on the differences between the distributions.

c The company has to get rid of 1 operator. Who should go and why?

★5 A school entered 80 pupils for an examination. The results are shown in the table.

Mark, x	$0 < x \leqslant 20$	$20 < x \leqslant 40$	$40 < x \leqslant 60$	$60 < x \leqslant 80$	$80 < x \leqslant 100$
Number of pupils	2	14	28	26	10

    a   Calculate an estimate of the mean.

    b   Complete a cumulative frequency table and draw a cumulative frequency diagram.

    c   **i**   Use your graph to estimate the median mark.

         ii   12 of these pupils were given a grade A. Use your graph to estimate the lowest mark for which grade A was given.

    d   Another school also entered 80 pupils for the same examination. Their results were Lowest mark 40, Lower quartile 50, Median 60, Upper quartile 70, Highest mark 80. Draw a box plot to show these results and use it to comment on the differences between the two schools' results.

HOMEWORK 18F

Use your calculator to work out the answers.

1   Find the mean and standard deviation of the following sets of data.

    a   4, 7, 8, 8, 11   **b**   17, 19, 21, 23, 28   **c**   82, 85, 88, 89, 92

    d   201, 202, 203, 204, 205   **e**   65, 71, 76, 76   **f**   −4, −2, −1, 0, 2, 5, 7

    g   91, 92, 98, 100, 105   **h**   29, 32, 35, 36, 42, 43

2   **a**   Calculate the mean and the standard deviation of 6, 8, 11, 14, 15, 18.

    b   Write down the mean and standard deviation of 16, 18, 21, 24, 25, 28.

    c   Write down the mean and the standard deviation of 60, 80, 110, 140, 150, 180.

3   Five numbers, 4, 8, 10, x and y, have a mean of 10 and a standard deviation of 4. Find the values of x and y.

4   In the 1996 Northern Counties Road Relays, teams of six runners each ran a 4-mile leg. The three winning teams had these times for each of their six runners.

        First team: Salford Harriers   19.50, 19.47, 19.43, 19.30, 20.01, 19.40

        Second team: Bingley Harriers   19.42, 20.32, 20.09, 19.50, 19.34, 19.36

        Third team: Sunderland   20.40, 20.40, 20.36, 19.23, 20.29, 19.45

    a   Calculate the mean and the standard deviation of each team. (Remember that the times above are in minutes and seconds.)

    b   One of the top three teams has to be chosen to represent Northern Counties at the National Road Relays. Which team should be chosen and why?

HOMEWORK 18G

Use your calculator to work out the answers.

1   The number of eggs in 20 nests in a wood are

    3, 6, 5, 8, 3, 4, 5, 7, 7, 8, 3, 9, 3, 6, 2, 6, 5, 8, 7, 2

    Put these numbers into a frequency table and calculate the mean and the standard deviation of the number of eggs per nest.

2   Calculate the mean and the standard deviation of the data in these tables.

a

x	f
0	3
1	5
2	9
3	5
4	3

b

x	f
122	4
123	6
124	7
125	6
126	4
127	3

c

x	f
100	3
101	5
102	9
103	5
104	3

3   The tables below show the results of two classes in a mathematics test.

Class 1

Mark, x	0	1	2	3	4	5	6	7	8	9	10
Frequency, f	0	1	4	6	5	4	5	6	1	2	1

Class 2

Mark, x	0	1	2	3	4	5	6	7	8	9	10
Frequency, f	0	0	2	2	10	11	5	4	1	1	0

a   Calculate the mean and the standard deviation for each class.

b   Which class did better in the test? Why?

4   During the first six weeks in a new job Mrs Best recorded how long it took her from getting out of bed to walking through the office door. The results are shown in the table.

Time, x (min)	80	85	90	95	100	105
Frequency, f	6	4	10	5	3	2

a   Calculate the mean and the standard deviation of the data.

b   Mrs Best has to arrive at work by 9.00 am. If she is late more than five times in a 30-day period, she will be sacked. She decides to set her alarm for 7.30 am. Is this a good idea? Justify your answer.

19   Probability

HOMEWORK 19A

1   Kylie takes a ball at random from a bag that contains six red and four white balls. The table shows her results.

Number of draws	10	20	50	100	500
Number of white balls	2	6	18	42	192

a   Calculate the relative frequency of a white ball at each stage that Kylie recorded her results.

b   What is the theoretical probability of taking a white ball from the bag?

c   If Kylie took a ball out of the bag a total of 5000 times, how many white balls would you expect her to get?

2 Jason made a six-sided spinner. To test it he threw it 600 times. The table shows the results.

Number	1	2	3	4	5	6
Total	98	152	85	102	62	101

a Work out the relative frequency of each number.

b How many times would you expect each number to occur if the spinner is fair?

c Do you think that the spinner is fair? Give a reason for your answer.

3 A bag contains red, white and blue balls. It is known that there are 50 balls in the bag altogether. Mary performs an experiment to see how many of each colour are in the bag. She counts up the tallies and records them in a table.

a Calculate the relative frequencies of the balls at each stage to 3 sf.

b How many of each colour do you think are in the bag? Explain your answer.

Red	White	Blue	Total
31	52	17	100
68	120	62	250
102	203	95	400
127	252	121	500

4 Which of these methods would you use to estimate or state the probability of each of the events **a** to **g**?

Method A: Equally likely outcomes   Method B: Survey or experiment

Method C: Look at historical data

a There will be an earthquake in Japan.

b The next person to walk through the door will be female.

c A Premier League team will win the FA Cup.

d You will win a raffle.

e The next car to drive down the road will be foreign.

f You will have a Maths lesson this week.

g A person picked at random from your school will go abroad for their holiday.

★5 A bag contains a number of counters. Each counter is coloured red, blue or yellow. Each counter is numbered 1 or 2. The table shows the probability of the colour and number for those counters.

Number of counter	Colour of counter		
	Red	Blue	Yellow
1	0.2	0.3	0.1
2	0.2	0.1	0.1

a A counter is taken from the bag at random. What is the probability that

   i it is red **and** numbered 2   **ii** it is blue **or** numbered 2

   iii it is red **or** numbered 2?

b There are two yellow counters in the bag. How many counters are in the bag altogether?

HOMEWORK 19B

1 Say whether these pairs of events are mutually exclusive or not.

a Tossing two heads with two coins/tossing two tails with two coins.

b Throwing an even number with a dice/throwing an odd number with a dice.

c Drawing a Queen from a pack of cards/drawing an Ace from a pack of cards.

d Drawing a Queen from a pack of cards/drawing a red card from a pack of cards.

e Drawing a red card from a pack of cards/drawing a heart from a pack of cards.

2   Which of the pairs of mutually exclusive events in Question **1** are also exhaustive?

3   A letter is to be chosen at random from this set of letter-cards.
MISSISSIPPI
   a   What is the probability the letter is
     i   an S   **ii**   a P   **iii**   a vowel?
   b   Which of these pairs of events are mutually exclusive?
     i   Picking an S / picking a P.   **ii**   Picking an S / picking an I.
     iii   Picking an I / picking a consonant.
   c   Which pair of mutually exclusive events in part **b** is also exhaustive?

4   Two people are to be chosen for a job from this set of six people.
     Ann   Joan   Jack   John   Arthur   Ethel
   a   List all of the possible pairs (there are 15 altogether).
   b   What is the probability that the pair of people chosen will be
     i   both female   **ii**   both male   **iii**   both have the same initial
     iv   have different initials?
   c   Which of these pairs of events are mutually exclusive?
     i   Picking two women / picking two men.
     ii   Picking two people of the same sex / picking two people of opposite sex.
     iii   Picking two people with the same initial / picking two men.
     iv   Picking two people with the same initial / picking two women.
   d   Which pair of mutually exclusive events in part **c** is also exhaustive?

5   For breakfast I like to have toast, porridge or cereal. The probability I have toast is $\frac{1}{3}$, the probability I have porridge is $\frac{1}{2}$, what is the probability I have cereal?

6   A person is chosen at random. Here is a list of events.
     Event A: the person chosen is male   Event B: the person chosen is female
     Event C: the person chosen is over 18   Event D: the person chosen is under 16
     Event E: the person chosen has a degree   Event F: the person chosen is a teacher
   For each of the pairs of events **i** to **x**, say whether they are
   a   mutually exclusive   **b**   exhaustive.
   c   If they are not mutually exclusive, explain why.
     i   Event A and Event B   **ii**   Event A and Event C
     iii   Event B and Event D   **iv**   Event C and Event D
     v   Event D and Event F   **vi**   Event E and Event F
     vii   Event E and Event D   **viii**   Event A and Event E
     ix   Event C and Event F   **x**   Event C and Event E

★7   An amateur weather man records the weather over a year in his village. He knows that the probability of a windy day is 0.4 and that the probability of a rainy day is 0.6. Steve says 'This means it will be either rainy or windy each day as 0.4 + 0.6 = 1, which is certain.' Explain why Steve is wrong.

HOMEWORK 19C

1   I throw an ordinary dice 600 times. How many times can I expect to get a score of 1?

2   I toss a coin 500 times. How many times can I expect to get a tail?

3   I draw a card from a pack of cards and replace it. I do this 104 times. How many times would I expect to get
   a   a red card   **b**   a Queen   **c**   a red seven
   d   the Jack of Diamonds?

4 The ball in a roulette wheel can land on any number from 0 to 36. I always bet on the same block of numbers 0–6. If I play all evening and there is a total of 111 spins of the wheel in that time, how many times could I expect to win?

5 I have five tickets for a raffle and I know that the probability of my winning the prize is 0.003. How many tickets were sold altogether in the raffle?

6 In a bag there are 20 balls, ten of which are red, three yellow, and seven blue. A ball is taken out at random and then replaced. This is repeated 200 times. How many times would I expect to get
  a a red ball   **b** a yellow or blue ball
  c a ball that is not blue   **d** a green ball?

7 A sampling bottle contains black and white balls. It is known that the probability of getting a black ball is 0.4. How many white balls would you expect to get in 200 samples?

8 **a** Fred is about to take his driving test. The chance he passes is $\frac{1}{3}$. His sister says 'Don't worry if you fail because you are sure to pass within three attempts because $3 \times \frac{1}{3} = 1$'. Explain why his sister is wrong.
  b If Fred does fail would you expect the chance that he passes next time to increase or decrease? Explain your answer.

★9 An opinion poll used a sample of 200 voters in one area. 112 said they would vote for Party A. There are a total of 50 000 voters in the area.
  a If they all voted, how many would you expect to vote for Party A?
  b The poll is accurate within 10%. Can Party A be confident of winning?

HOMEWORK 19D

1 The two way table shows the number of children and the number of computers in 40 homes in one road in a town.

Number of computers	Number of children			
	0	1	2	3
0	3	0	0	0
1	4	10	2	2
2	0	4	9	3
3	0	0	2	1

  a How many homes have exactly two children and two computers?
  b How many homes altogether have two computers?
  c What percentage of the homes have two computers?
  d What percentage of the homes with just one child have one computer?

2 The two way table shows the part time earnings of a set of students during one summer break.

Earnings per week	Male	Female
£0 < E ≤ £50	4	1
£50 < E ≤ £100	4	1
£100 < E ≤ £150	11	4
£150 < E ≤ £200	24	14
£200 < E ≤ £250	16	10
More than £250	2	1

a What percentage of the male students earned between £100 and £150 per week?

b What percentage of the female students earned between £100 and £150 per week?

c Estimate the mean earnings of this set of students.

d Which sex has the greater estimated mean earnings? Explain how you might do this without doing the actual calculation.

HOMEWORK 19E

1 Shaheeb throws an ordinary dice. What is the probability that he throws
   a an even number   **b** 5   **c** an even number or 5?

2 Jane draws a card from a pack of cards. What is the probability that she draws
   a a red card   **b** a black card   **c** a red or a black card?

3 Natalie draws a card from a pack of cards. What is the probability that she draws one of the following numbers?
   a Ace   **b** King   **c** Ace or King

4 A letter is chosen at random from the letters in the word STATISTICS. What is the probability that the letter will be
   a S   **b** a vowel   **c** S or a vowel?

5 A bag contains ten white balls, 12 black balls and eight red balls. A ball is drawn at random from the bag. What is the probability that it will be
   a white   **b** black   **c** black or white
   d not red   **e** not red or black?

6 A spinner has numbers and colours on it, as shown in the diagram. Their probabilities are given in the tables.

Red	0.5
Green	0.25
Blue	0.25

1	0.4
2	0.35
3	0.25

When the spinner is spun what is the probability of each of the following?
   a Red or blue   **b** 2 or 3   **c** 3 or blue   **d** 2 or green
   e **i** Explain why the answer to **c** is 0.25 and not 0.5.
        ii What is the answer to P(2 or red)?

7 Debbie has ten CDs in her multi-changer, four of which are rock, two are dance and four are classical. She puts the player on random play. What is the probability that the first CD will be
   a rock or dance   **b** rock or classical   **c** not rock?

8 Frank buys one dozen free-range eggs. The farmer tells him that a quarter of the eggs his hens lay have double yolks.
   a How many eggs with double yolks can Frank expect to get?
   b He cooks three and finds they all have a single yolk. He argues that he now has a 1 in 3 chance of a double yolk from the remaining eggs. Explain why he is wrong.

★9 John has a bag containing six red, five blue and four green balls. One ball is picked from the bag at random. What is the probability that the ball is
   a red or blue   **b** not blue   **c** pink   **d** red or not blue?

1 Two dice are thrown together. Draw a probability diagram to show the total score.
   a What is the probability of a score that is
      i 7 ii 5 or 8 iii bigger than 9 iv between 2 and 5
      v odd vi a non-square number?

2 Two dice are thrown. Draw a probability diagram to show the outcomes as pairs of co-ordinates.
   What is the probability that
   a the score is a 'double'
   b at least one of the dice shows 3
   c the score on one dice is three times the score on the other dice
   d at least one of the dice shows an odd number
   e both dice show a 5
   f at least one of the dice will show a 5
   g exactly one dice shows a 5?

3 Two dice are thrown. The score on one dice is doubled and the score on the other dice is subtracted.
   Complete the probability space diagram.
   For the event described above, what is the probability of a score of
   a 1
   b a negative number
   c an even number
   d 0 or 1
   e a prime number?

Score on second dice						
6						6
5						
4						
3	−1					
2	0					
1	1	3	5	7	9	11
	1	2	3	4	5	6

   Score on first dice

4 When two coins are tossed together, what is the probability of
   a two heads or two tails   b a head and a tail   c at least one head?

5 When three coins are tossed together, what is the probability of
   a three heads or three tails   b two tails and one head   c at least one head?

6 When a dice and a coin are thrown together, what is the probability of each of the following outcomes?
   a You get a tail on the coin and a 3 on the dice.
   b You get a head on the coin and an odd number on the dice.

★7 Max buys two bags of bulbs from his local garden centre. Each bag has four bulbs. Two bulbs are daffodils, one is a tulip and one is hyacinth. Max takes one bulb from each bag.
   a There are six possible different pairs of bulbs. List them all.
   b Complete the sample space diagram.
   c What is the probability of getting two daffodil bulbs?
   d Explain why the answer is not $\frac{1}{6}$.

Hyac				HH
Tulip	DT			
Daff				
Daff	DD	DD	TD	
	Daff	Daff	Tulip	Hyac

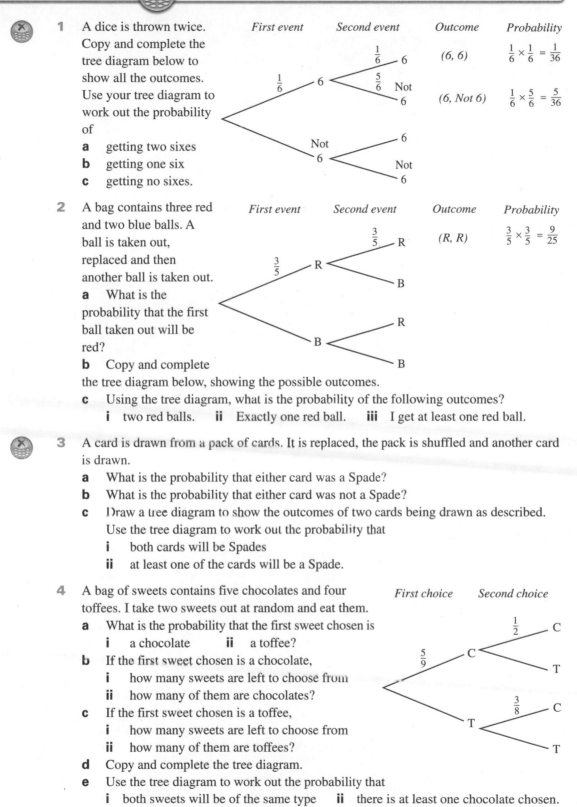

1   A dice is thrown twice. *First event* *Second event* *Outcome* *Probability*
Copy and complete the
tree diagram below to
show all the outcomes.
Use your tree diagram to
work out the probability
of
a   getting two sixes
b   getting one six
c   getting no sixes.

$\frac{1}{6} \times \frac{1}{6} = \frac{1}{36}$ for outcome (6, 6)

$\frac{1}{6} \times \frac{5}{6} = \frac{5}{36}$ for outcome (6, Not 6)

2   A bag contains three red   *First event* *Second event* *Outcome* *Probability*
and two blue balls. A
ball is taken out,
replaced and then
another ball is taken out.
a   What is the
probability that the first
ball taken out will be
red?
b   Copy and complete
the tree diagram below, showing the possible outcomes.
c   Using the tree diagram, what is the probability of the following outcomes?
  i   two red balls.   **ii**   Exactly one red ball.   **iii**   I get at least one red ball.

(R, R) with probability $\frac{3}{5} \times \frac{3}{5} = \frac{9}{25}$

3   A card is drawn from a pack of cards. It is replaced, the pack is shuffled and another card
is drawn.
a   What is the probability that either card was a Spade?
b   What is the probability that either card was not a Spade?
c   Draw a tree diagram to show the outcomes of two cards being drawn as described.
Use the tree diagram to work out the probability that
  i   both cards will be Spades
  ii   at least one of the cards will be a Spade.

4   A bag of sweets contains five chocolates and four   *First choice*   *Second choice*
toffees. I take two sweets out at random and eat them.
a   What is the probability that the first sweet chosen is
  i   a chocolate   **ii**   a toffee?
b   If the first sweet chosen is a chocolate,
  i   how many sweets are left to choose from
  ii   how many of them are chocolates?
c   If the first sweet chosen is a toffee,
  i   how many sweets are left to choose from
  ii   how many of them are toffees?
d   Copy and complete the tree diagram.
e   Use the tree diagram to work out the probability that
  i   both sweets will be of the same type   **ii**   there is at least one chocolate chosen.

5   Thomas has to take a driving test which is in two parts. The first part is theoretical. He
has a 0.4 chance of passing this. The second is practical. He has a 0.5 chance of passing
this. Draw a tree diagram covering passing or failing the two parts of the test. What is the
probability that he passes both parts?

6 Every Sunday morning Carol goes out for a run. She has three pairs of shorts of which two are red and one is blue. She has five T-shirts of which three are red and two are blue. Because she can't disturb her husband she gets dressed in the dark and picks a pair of shorts and a T-shirt at random.

    a What is the probability that the shorts are blue?

    b Copy and complete this tree diagram.

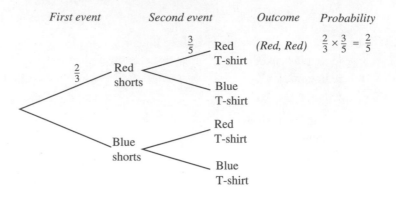

    c What is the probability that Carol goes running in
      i a matching pair of shorts and T-shirt
      ii a mis-match of shorts and T-shirt
      iii at least one red item?

★7 Bob has a bag containing four blue balls, five red balls and one green ball. Sally has a bag containing two blue balls and three red balls. The balls are identical except for the colour. Bob chooses a ball at random from his bag and Sally chooses a ball at random from her bag.

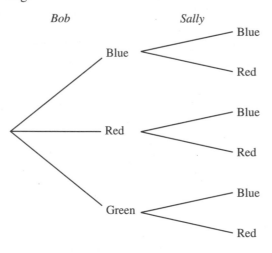

    a On a copy of the tree diagram, write the probability of each of the events on the appropriate branch.

    b Calculate the probability that both Bob and Sally will choose a blue ball.

    c Calculate the probability that the ball chosen by Bob will be a different colour from the ball chosen by Sally.

HOMEWORK 19H

1 Ahmed throws a dice twice. The dice is biased so the probability of getting a six is $\frac{1}{4}$. What is the probability that he gets

    a two sixes   **b** exactly one six?

2 Betty draws a card from a pack of cards, replaces it, shuffles the pack and then draws another card. What is the probability that the cards are
   a both Hearts   **b** a Heart and a Spade (in any order)?

3 Colin draws a card from a pack of cards, does not replace it and then draws another card. What is the probability that the cards are
   a both Hearts   **b** a Heart and a Spade (in any order)?

4 I throw a dice three times. What is the probability of getting a total score of 17 or 18?

5 A bag contains seven white beads and three black beads. I take out a bead at random, replace it and take out another bead. What is the probability that
   a both beads are black   **b** one bead is black and the other white (in any order)?

6 A bag contains seven white beads and three black beads. I take out a bead at random, do not replace it and take out another bead. What is the probability that
   a both beads are black   **b** one bead is black and the other white (in any order)?

★7 When I answer the telephone the call is never for me. Half the calls are for my daughter Janette. One-third of them are for my son Glen. The rest are for my wife Barbara.
   a I answer the telephone twice this evening. Calculate the probability that
      i the first call will be for Barbara   **ii** both calls will be for Barbara.
   b The probability that both these calls are for Janette is $\frac{1}{4}$. The probability that they are both for Glen is $\frac{1}{9}$. Calculate the probability that either they are both for Janette or both for Glen.

HOMEWORK 19I

1 Steve eats in the school canteen five days a week. The probability that there is turnip on the menu on any day is $\frac{1}{4}$.
   a What is the probability that in five days there is no turnip on the menu?
   b What is the probability that Steve gets turnip at least once in five days?

2 Three coins are thrown. What is the probability of
   a three tails   **b** at least one head?

3 Adam is a talented all-round athlete. He is entered for the 100 m race, the javelin and the high jump. The probability that he wins each of these events is $\frac{4}{5}$, $\frac{3}{4}$ and $\frac{1}{2}$ respectively.
   a What is the probability that he doesn't win any event?
   b What is the probability that he wins at least one event?

4 A bag contains seven red and three blue balls. A ball is taken out and replaced. Another ball is taken out. What is the probability that
   a both balls are red   **b** both balls are blue   **c** at least one is red?

5 A bag contains seven red and three blue balls. A ball is taken out and not replaced. Another ball is taken out. What is the probability that
   a both balls are red   **b** both balls are blue   **c** at least one is red?

6 **a** A coin is thrown three times. What is the probability of
      i three heads   **ii** no heads   **iii** at least one head?
   b A coin is thrown four times. What is the probability of
      i four heads   **ii** no heads   **iii** at least one head?
   c A coin is thrown five times. What is the probability of
      i five heads   **ii** no heads   **iii** at least one head?
   d A coin is thrown n times. What is the probability of
      i n heads   **ii** no heads   **iii** at least one head?

7 A class has 12 boys and 14 girls. Three of the class are to be chosen at random to do a task for their teacher. What is the probability that

    a all three are girls   **b** at least one is a boy?

★8 From three boys and two girls, two children are to be chosen to present a bouquet of flowers to the Mayoress. The children are to be selected by drawing their names out of a hat. What is the probability that

    a there will be a boy and a girl chosen

    b there will be two boys chosen

    c there will be at least one girl chosen?

HOMEWORK 19J

1 A bag contains two black balls and five red balls. A ball is taken out and replaced. This is repeated twice. What is the probability that

    a all three are black   **b** exactly two are black

    c exactly 1 is black   **d** none is black?

2 A bag contains two blue balls and five white balls. A ball is taken out but not replaced. This is repeated twice. What is the probability that

    a all three are blue   **b** exactly two are blue

    c exactly 1 is blue   **d** none is blue?

3 A dice is thrown three times. What is the probability that

    a four sixes are thrown   **b** no sixes are thrown   **c** exactly one six is thrown?

4 Ann is late for school with a probability of 0.7. Bob is late with a probability of 0.6. Cedrick is late with a probability of 0.3. On any particular day what is the probability of

    a exactly one of them being late   **b** exactly two of them being late?

5 Daisy takes three AS exams in Mathematics. The probability that she will pass Pure 1 is 0.9. The probability that she will pass Statistics 1 is 0.65. The probability she will pass Discrete 1 is 0.95. What is the probability that she will pass

    a all three modules   **b** exactly two modules   **c** at least two modules?

6 six out of ten cars in Britain run on petrol. The rest use diesel fuel. Three cars can be seen approaching in the distance.

    a What is the probability that the first one uses petrol?

    b What is the probability that exactly two of them use diesel fuel?

    c Explain why, if the first car uses petrol, the probability of the second car using petrol is still 6 out of 10.

★7 In a class of 30 pupils, 21 have dark hair, seven have fair hair and two have red hair. Two pupils are chosen at random to collect homework. What is the probabilty that they

    a both have fair hair

    b each have hair of a different colour?

    c If three pupils are chosen, what is the probability that exactly two have dark hair?

HOMEWORK 19K

1 A bag contains five black and three white balls. Three balls are taken out one at a time.

    a If the balls are put back each time, what is the probability of getting

        i three black balls   **ii** at least one black ball?

    b If the balls are not put back each time, what is the probability of getting

        i three black balls   **ii** at least one black ball?

2 Two cards are drawn one at a time from a pack of cards. The cards are replaced each time. What is the probability that at least one of them is a Heart?

3 Two cards are drawn from a pack of cards. The cards are not replaced each time. What is the probability that at least one of them is a Heart?

4 A box contains 50 batteries. It is known that 20 of them are dead. John needs two batteries for his calculator. He takes three out. What is the probability that
   a   all three of them are dead   **b**   at least one of them works?

5 From the same box of 100 batteries (Question **4**), Janet takes out three batteries for her radio. The radio will work if two or three of the batteries are good. What is the probability that the radio will work?

6 Two tetrahedral (four-sided) dice, whose faces are numbered 1, 2, 3 and 4, are thrown together. The score on the dice is the uppermost face. Show by means of a sample space diagram that there are 16 outcomes with total scores from 2 to 8. What is the probability of
   a   a total score of 8   **b**   at least one 3 on either dice?

7 Based on previous results the probability that Manchester United win is $\frac{2}{3}$, the probability they draw is $\frac{1}{4}$ and the probability they lose is $\frac{1}{12}$.
They play three matches. What is the probability that
   a   they win all three   **b**   they win exactly two matches
   c   they win at least one match?

8 In the Spark'n, Spit'n and Fizz'n machine, the probability that the Spark fails is 0.02. The probability that the Spit fails is 0.08 and the probability that the Fizz fails is 0.05.
   a   What is the probability that nothing fails?
   b   The machine will still work with one component out of action. What is the probability that it works?

9 On average, Steve is late for school two days each week (of five days).
   a   What is the probability that he is late on any one day?
   b   In a week of five days, what is the probability that
      i   he is late every day   **ii**   he is late exactly once
      iii   he is never late   **iv**   he is late at least once?

10 Six T-shirts are hung out at random on a washing line. Three are red and three are blue. Using R and B, write down all 20 possible combinations: for example, RRRBBB, RRBBBR, …. What is the probability of
   a   three red shirts being next to each other
   b   three blue shirts being next to each other?

11 Dan has six socks in a drawer, of which four are blue and two are black. He takes out two socks. What is the probability that
   a   both socks are blue   **b**   both socks are black
   c   he gets a pair of socks   **d**   at least one of the socks is blue?

12 One in nine people are left-handed. Five people are in a room. What is the probability that
   a   all five are left-handed   **b**   all five are right-handed
   c   at least one of them is left-handed?

13 A maze is tilted slightly to the left. A ball is dropped into a maze at *A*. It can go left with a probability of $\frac{2}{3}$ and right with a probability of $\frac{1}{3}$.

  a Show that the probability that the ball lands in slot 1 is $\frac{8}{27}$.

  b Show that the probability that the ball lands in slot 2 is $\frac{12}{27}$.

  c 54 balls are dropped into the maze at *A*. How many would you expect to land in slot 4?

★**14** There are five yellow counters in a bag of nine coloured counters. Three counters are taken out of the bag at random, one at a time and without replacement.

  a Find the probability that exactly two of the three counters are yellow.

  A group of students do an experiment with the bag of nine coloured counters. They take two counters from the bag at random, one at a time and without replacement. They record the colour of each counter and then put the two counters back in the bag. They repeat this experiment 1000 times. They find that the relative frequency of taking two red counters from the bag is 0.083.

  b **i** How many times were two red counters taken out of the bag?

   ii Show that three is a good estimate of the most likely number of red counters in the bag.

20 Algebra 3

HOMEWORK 20A

1 Simplify each of these.

  a $\dfrac{2x}{3} + \dfrac{4x}{5}$
  b $\dfrac{x+1}{3} + \dfrac{x+3}{2}$
  c $\dfrac{2x-3}{2} + \dfrac{5x-1}{3}$

2 Simplify each of these.

  a $\dfrac{3x}{4} - \dfrac{2x}{5}$
  b $\dfrac{x+2}{2} - \dfrac{x+1}{5}$
  c $\dfrac{4x-1}{2} - \dfrac{2x-4}{3}$

3 Solve the following equations

  a $\dfrac{2x}{3} + \dfrac{4x}{5} = 11$
  b $\dfrac{x+1}{3} + \dfrac{x+3}{2} = 10$
  c $\dfrac{2x-5}{2} - \dfrac{x-1}{3} = 1$

4 Simplify each of these.

  a $\dfrac{3x}{2} \times \dfrac{4x}{5}$
  b $\dfrac{x+1}{4} \times \dfrac{3}{2x+2}$
  c $\dfrac{2x-1}{2} \times \dfrac{4}{3x-1}$

5 Simplify each of these.

  a $\dfrac{x}{4} \div \dfrac{2x}{5}$
  b $\dfrac{x+3}{2} \div \dfrac{2x+6}{5}$
  c $\dfrac{4x-2}{3} \div \dfrac{2x-1}{4}$

6 Show that $\dfrac{3}{x+2} + \dfrac{5}{2x-1} = 2$ simplifies to $4x^2 - 5x - 11 = 0$

7 Solve the following equations.

a $\dfrac{3}{x-1} + \dfrac{2}{2x+3} = 5$ **b** $\dfrac{5}{3x+2} - \dfrac{3}{2x-3} = 4$

8 Simplify the expression $\dfrac{x^2 - 2x - 3}{2x^2 - 10x + 12}$

HOMEWORK 20B

Solve the following pairs of simultaneous equations

1 $xy = 3$
    $y = x - 2$

2 $xy = 2$
    $2y - x = 3$

3 $x^2 + y^2 = 29$
    $x - y = 7$

4 $y = x^2 + 3x + 4$
    $y = 1 - x$

5 $y = x^2 - 3x + 5$
    $y = 2x - 1$

6 $y = 4x^2 + 2x + 1$
    $y = 3x^2 + 2x + 2$

HOMEWORK 20C

1 Look at the following number sequences. Write down the next three terms in each and explain how each sequence is found.

   a   4, 6, 8, 10, …   **b**   3, 6, 9, 12, …   **c**   2, 4, 8, 16, …
   d   5, 12, 19, 26, …   **e**   3, 30, 300, 3000, …   **f**   1, 4, 9, 16, …

2 Look carefully at each number sequence below. Find the next two numbers in the sequence and try to explain the pattern.

   a   1, 2, 3, 5, 8, 13, 21, …   **b**   2, 3, 5, 8, 12, 17, …

3 Look at the sequences below. Find the rule for each sequence and write down its next three terms.

   a   7, 14, 28, 56, …   **b**   3, 10, 17, 24, 31, …   **c**   1, 3, 7, 15, 31, …
   d   40, 39, 37, 34, …   **e**   3, 6, 11, 18, 27, …   **f**   4, 5, 7, 10, 14, 19, …
   g   4, 6, 7, 9, 10, 12, …   **h**   5, 8, 11, 14, 17, …   **i**   5, 7, 10, 14, 19, 25, …
   j   10, 9, 7, 4, …   **k**   200, 40, 8, 1.6, …   **l**   3, 1.5, 0.75, 0.375, …

HOMEWORK 20D

1 Find the nth term in each of these linear sequences.

   a   5, 7, 9, 11, 13 …   **b**   3, 7, 11, 15, 19, …   **c**   6, 11, 16, 21, 26, …
   d   3, 9, 15, 21, 27, …   **e**   4, 7, 10, 13, 16, …   **f**   3, 10, 17, 24, 31, …

2 Find the 50th term in each of these linear sequences.

   a   3, 5, 7, 9, 11, …   **b**   5, 9, 13, 17, 21, …   **c**   8, 13, 18, 23, 28, …
   d   2, 8, 14, 20, 26, …   **e**   5, 8, 11, 14, 17, …   **f**   2, 9, 16, 23, 30, …

3 For each sequence **a** to **f**, find

   i   the nth term   **ii**   the 100th term   **iii**   the term closest to 100

   a   4, 7, 10, 13, 16, …   **b**   7, 9, 11, 13, 15, …   **c**   3, 8, 13, 18, 23, …
   d   1, 5, 9, 13, 17, …   **e**   2, 10, 18, 26, …   **f**   5, 6, 7, 8, 9, …

4 A sequence of fractions is $\dfrac{3}{5}, \dfrac{5}{8}, \dfrac{7}{11}, \dfrac{9}{14}, …$

   a   Find the nth term in the sequence.   **b**   Change each fraction to a decimal.
   c   What, as a decimal, will be the value of the   **i**   100th term   **ii**   1000th term?
   d   Use your answers to part **c** to predict what the 10 000th term and the millionth term are. (Check these out on your calculator.)

★5 **a** A number pattern begins 1, 1, 2, 3, 5, 8, ...

    i What is the next number in this pattern?

    ii The number pattern is continued. Explain how you would find the tenth number in the pattern.

b Another number pattern begins 1, 5, 9, 13, 17, ... Write down, in terms of n, the nth term in this pattern.

6 p is an even number, q is a square number.

State if the following are odd or even or could be either odd or even.

a $p + 1$ **b** $p + q$ **c** $2q$ **d** $3p - 1$

e p^2 **f** $pq - 1$ **g** $p^2 + 4q$ **h** $(p + q)(p - q)$

HOMEWORK 20E

1 A pattern of shapes is built up from matchsticks as shown.

a Draw the fourth diagram.

b How many matchsticks are in the nth diagram?

c How many matchsticks are in the 25th diagram?

d With 200 matchsticks, which is the biggest diagram that could be made?

2 A pattern of hexagons is built up from matchsticks.

a Draw the fourth set of hexagons in this pattern.

b How many matchsticks are needed for the nth set of hexagons?

c How many matchsticks are needed to make the 60th set of hexagons?

d If there are only 100 matchsticks, which is the largest set of hexagons that could be made?

3 A conference centre had tables each of which could sit three people. When put together, the tables could seat people as shown.

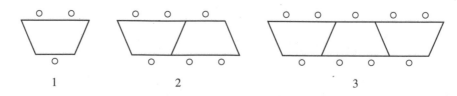

a How many people could be seated at four tables?

b How many people could be seated at n tables put together in this way?

c A conference had 50 people who wished to use the tables in this way. How many tables would they need?

4 A pattern of squares is put together as shown.

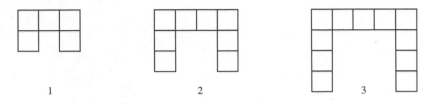

1   2   3

    a Draw the fourth diagram.
    b How many squares are in the nth diagram?
    c How many squares are in the 50th diagram?
    d With 300 squares, work out the number of the biggest diagram that could be made.

★**5** Sheep enclosures are built using fences and posts.

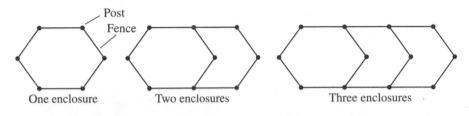

One enclosure   Two enclosures   Three enclosures

    a **i** Sketch four enclosures in a row.   **ii** Sketch five enclosures in a row.
    b Copy and complete the table below.

Number of enclosures	1	2	3	4	5	6	7	8
Number of posts	6	9	12					

    c Work out the number of posts needed for 20 enclosures in a row.
    d Write down an expression to find the number of posts needed for n enclosures in a row.

HOMEWORK 20F

1 For each of the sequences **a** to **e**
    i write down the next two terms   **ii** find the nth term.
    a 1, 4, 9, 16, 25, …   **b** 2, 5, 10, 17, 26, …   **c** 5, 8, 13, 20, 29, …
    d 2, 8, 18, 32, 50, …   **e** 21, 24, 29, 36, 45, …

2 For each of the sequences **a** to **e**
    i write down the next two terms   **ii** find the nth term.
    a 4, 10, 18, 28, …   **b** 15, 24, 35, 48, …   **c** 2, 6, 12, 20, …
    d 1, 3, 6, 10, …   **e** 6, 12, 20, 30, …

3 Look at each of the following sequences to see whether the rule is linear, quadratic on n^2 alone or fully quadratic. Then
    i write down the nth term   **ii** write down the 50th term.
    a 8, 13, 20, 29, …   **b** 8, 11, 14, 17, …   **c** 8, 15, 24, 35, …
    d 0, 5, 12, 21, 32, 45, …

★**4**   The picture shows a pattern of cards.

1 storey   2 storeys   3 storeys   4 storeys
2 cards   7 cards   15 cards   26 cards

a   The four-storey house of cards is to be made into a five-storey house of cards. How many more cards are needed?

b   Look at the sequence 2, 7, 15, 26, …

    i   Calculate the sixth term in this sequence.

    ii   Explain how you found your answer.

HOMEWORK 20G

In questions 1 to 5, make the stated term the subject of each formula.

1 $4(x - 2y) = 3(2x - y)$ (x) **2** $p(a - b) = q(a + b)$ (a)

3 $A = 2ab^2 + ac$ (a) **4** $s(t + 1) = 2r + 3$ (r)

5 $st - r = 2r - 3t$ (t)

6   Make x the subject of these equations.

    a $ax = b - cx$ **b** $x(a - b) = x + b$

    c $a - bx = dx - a$ **d** $x(c - d) = c(d - x)$

7   **a**   The perimeter of the shape on the right is given by $P = 2\pi r + 4r$
       Make r the subject of the formula.

    b   The area of the same shape is given by $A = \pi r^2 + 4r^2$
       Make r the subject of this formula.

8   **a**   Make x the subject of $y = \dfrac{x + 2}{x + 3}$

    b   Make x the subject of $y = \dfrac{2 - 3x}{x - 1}$

★**9**   Make a the subject of $a = \dfrac{2 + 3a}{b - 2}$

10   The resistance when two resistors with values a and b are connected in parallel is given by

$$R = \frac{ab}{a + b}$$

a   Make b the subject of the formula.

b   Write down the formula when a is the subject.

Find an expression for the perimeter of each of these shapes.

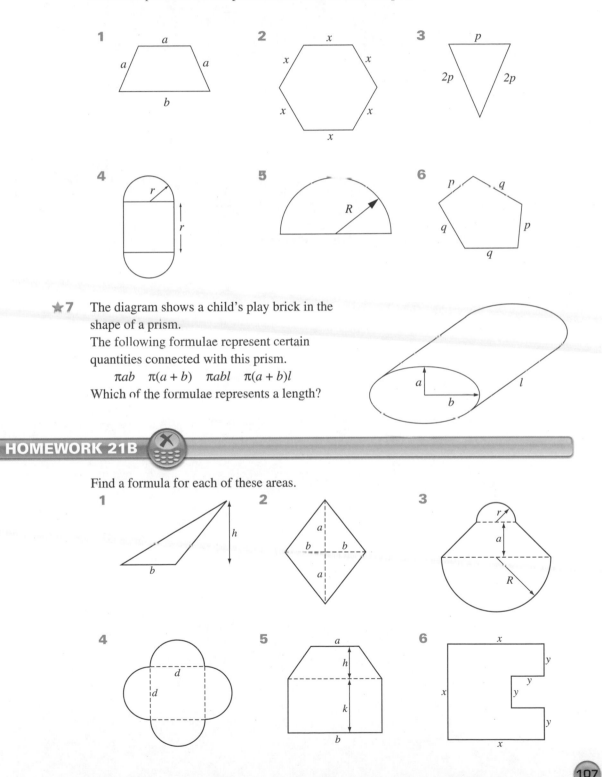

1

a

a a

b

2

x

x x

x x

x

3

p

$2p$ $2p$

4

r

r

5

R

6

p q

q p

q

★**7** The diagram shows a child's play brick in the shape of a prism.
The following formulae represent certain quantities connected with this prism.

$$\pi ab \quad \pi(a + b) \quad \pi abl \quad \pi(a + b)l$$

Which of the formulae represents a length?

a

b

l

Find a formula for each of these areas.

1

h

b

2

a

b b

a

3

r

a

R

4

d

d

5

a

h

k

b

6

x

y

y

x y

y

x

★7 One of the formulae in the list below can be used to calculate the area of material in a lampshade. Which formula is it?

   a $\pi h(a+b)^2$ **b** $\pi h^2(a+b)$ **c** $\pi h(a+b)$ **d** $\pi h^2(a+b)^2$

HOMEWORK 21C

Find a formula for each of these volumes.

1   **2**   **3**

4   **5**   **6**

★7 The dimensions of four cuboids are shown.

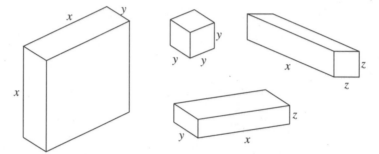

The expressions x^2y, xz and $2(x+y)$ give the perimeter of a face of one of the cuboids, or the area of a face of one of the cuboids, or the volume of one of the cuboids. Complete the statements below with the word perimeter, area or volume.

   a x^2y gives a ......   **b** $2(x+y)$ gives a ......   **c** xz gives an ....

HOMEWORK 21D

1 Indicate by L, A, V or [L], [L²], [L³] whether the following quantities are lengths, areas or volumes, or none of these (N).

   a   1 yard   **b**   12 hectares

   c   Paint in a can   **d**   Weight of this book

   e   Thickness of this book   **f**   Amount of paper used to print this book

   g   110 decibels   **h**   Amount of water flowing from a tap

   i   Latitude and longitude   **j**   m s^{-2}

2 Each of these represents a length, an area or a volume. Indicate by writing L, A or V which it is.

   a $ab+cd$ **b** a^2b+c^2d **c** $ab(c+d)$ **d** $\frac{4}{3}\pi r^3$

   e $\pi r^2+2\pi rh$ **f** $\frac{2}{3}\pi r^3+\pi r^2h$ **g** $\frac{ab+cb}{b}$ **h** $\frac{a^3b+b^3a}{c}$

★3 This diagram shows the cross-section of a barn. A farmer wants to estimate the area of a cross-section of a warehouse.

a Explain why the formula

$$A = \frac{H + 2W + L}{5}$$

cannot be a suitable formula for him to use.

b Look at these formulae.

i $A = \dfrac{4WHL}{5}$ ii $A = \dfrac{L(4H + 2W)}{5}$ iii $A = \dfrac{LW + 4H}{5}$

One of these formulae can be used to estimate the area of the cross-section. Which is it? Give a reason for your answer.

22 Variation

HOMEWORK 22A

In each case, first find k, the constant of proportionality, and then the formula connecting the variables.

1 T is directly proportional to M. If $T = 30$ when $M = 5$, find
   a T when $M = 4$ b M when $T = 75$

2 W is directly proportional to F. If $W = 54$ when $F = 3$, find
   a W when $F = 4$ b F when $W = 90$

3 P is directly proportional to A. If $P = 50$ when $A = 2$, find
   a P when $A = 5$ b A when $P = 150$

4 A is directly proportional to t. If $A = 45$ when $t = 5$, find
   a A when $t = 8$ b t when $A = 18$

5 Q varies directly with P. If $Q = 200$ when $P = 5$, find
   a Q when $P = 3$ b P when $Q = 300$

6 The distance covered by a train is directly proportional to the time taken. The train travels 135 miles in 3 hours.
   a What distance will the train cover in 4 hours?
   b What time will it take for the train to cover 315 miles?

7 The cost of petrol is directly proportional to the amount put in the tank. When 40 litres is used, it costs £32.00. How much
   a will it cost for 30 litres b would be delivered if the cost were £38.40?

8 The number of people who can meet safely in a room is directly proportional to the area of the room. A room with an area of 200 m² is safe for 50 people.
   a How many people can safely meet in a room of area 152 m²?
   b A committee has 24 members. What is the smallest room area in which they could safely meet?

★9 A man lays 36 paving stones in 3 hours. Working at the same rate how long would he take to lay 45 paving stones.

In each case, first find k, the constant of proportionality, and then the formula connecting the variables.

1 T is directly proportional to x^2. If $T = 40$ when $x = 2$, find
  a T when $x = 5$ **b** x when $T = 400$

2 W is directly proportional to M^2. If $W = 10$ when $M = 5$, find
  a W when $M = 4$ **b** M when $W = 64$

3 A is directly proportional to r^2. If $A = 96$ when $r = 4$, find
  a A when $r = 5$ **b** r when $A = 12$

4 E varies directly with $\sqrt{C}$. If $E = 60$ when $C = 36$, find
  a E when $C = 49$ **b** C when $E = 160$

5 X is directly proportional to $\sqrt{Y}$. If $X = 80$ when $Y = 16$, find
  a X when $Y = 100$ **b** Y when $X = 48$

6 H is directly proportional to $\sqrt{t}$. If $H = 20.8$ when $t = 4$, find
  a H when $t = 1.5$ **b** t when $H = 77.4$

7 P is directly proportional to f^3. If $P = 500$ when $f = 5$, find
  a P when $f = 4$ **b** f when $P = 50$

8 The temperature, in °C, in an experiment varied directly with the square of the pressure, in atmospheres. The temperature was 30 °C when the pressure was 6 atm. What will
  a the temperature be at 3 atm   **b** the pressure be at 90 °C?

★**9** The distance that can be seen out to sea on a clear day varies directly as the square root of the height above sea level. At a height of 6 metres above sea level, you can see 10 km on a clear day. What distance will you be able to see on a clear day from a height of 60 metres above sea level?

In each case, first find the formula connecting the variables.

1 T is inversely proportional to m. If $T = 7$ when $m = 4$, find
  a T when $m = 5$ **b** m when $T = 56$

2 W is inversely proportional to x. If $W = 6$ when $x = 15$, find
  a W when $x = 3$ **b** x when $W = 10$

3 M varies inversely with t^2. If $M = 10$ when $t = 2$, find
  a M when $t = 4$ **b** t when $M = 160$

4 C is inversely proportional to f^2. If $C = 20$ when $f = 3$, find
  a C when $f = 5$ **b** f when $C = 720$

5 W is inversely proportional to $\sqrt{T}$. If $W = 8$ when $T = 36$, find
  a W when $T = 25$ **b** T when $W = 0.75$

6 H varies inversely with $\sqrt{g}$. If $H = 20$ when $g = 16$, find
  a H when $g = 1.25$ **b** g when $H = 40$

7 The brightness of a bulb decreases inversely with the square of the distance away from the bulb. The brightness is 5 candle power at a distance of 10 metres. What is the brightness at a distance of 5 metres?

8 The density of a series of spheres with the same weight is inversely proportional to the cube of the radius. A sphere with a density of 10 g/cm³ has a radius of 5 cm.

  a What would be the density of a sphere with a radius of 10 cm?

  b If the density was 80 g/cm³ what would the radius of the sphere be?

★9 Given that y is inversely proportional to the square of x, and that y is 12 when $x = 4$,

  a find an expression for y in terms of x.

  b Calculate   **i** y when $x = 6$ **ii** x when $y = 36$

23 Number and limits of accuracy

HOMEWORK 23A

1 Write down the limits of accuracy for each of the following values which are to the given degree of accuracy.

a	7 cm (1 sf)	**b**	18 kg (2 sf)	**c**	30 min (2 sf)
d	747 km (3 sf)	**e**	9.8 m (1 dp)	**f**	32.1 kg (1 dp)
g	3.0 h (1 dp)	**h**	90 g (2 sf)	**i**	4.20 mm (2 dp)
j	2.00 kg (2 dp)	**k**	34.57 min (2 dp)	**l**	100 m (2 sf)

★2 Round off these numbers to the degree of accuracy given.

  a 45.678 to 3 sf   **b** 19.96 to 2 sf   **c** 0.3213 to 2 dp

HOMEWORK 23B

1 Write down the upper and lower bounds of each of these values given to the accuracy stated.

a	6 m (1 sf)	**b**	34 kg (2 sf)	**c**	56 min (2 sf)	**d**	80 g (2 sf)
e	3.70 m (2 dp)	**f**	0.9 kg (1 dp)	**g**	0.08 s (2 dp)	**h**	900 g (2 sf)
i	0.70 m (2 dp)	**j**	360 d (3 sf)	**k**	17 weeks (2 sf)	**l**	200 g (2 sf)

2 Billy has 20 identical bricks. Each brick is 15 cm long measured to the nearest centimetre.

  a What is the greatest length of one brick?

  b What is the smallest length of one brick?

  c If the bricks are put end to end, what is the greatest possible length of all the bricks?

  d If the bricks are put end to end, what is the least possible length of all the bricks?

★3 Cars are timed over a stretch of road using a digital timer which counts in tenths of a second. The digits change at the end of each complete tenth of a second. The time for one car is shown as 41.8 seconds.

  a Complete the inequality below to show the possible times taken by the car.
      ...... ⩽ time of car in seconds < ......

  b The stretch of road is 800 m long, correct to the nearest 10 metres. Calculate the minimum speed the car could have been travelling. Give your result in metres per second, correct to 2 decimal places.

  c Another car's speed is calculated as 31.73 metres per second (correct to 2 decimal places). Convert this speed to miles per hour. [1 metre per second = 2.237 miles per hour (correct to 3 decimal places).] Give your answer to an appropriate degree of accuracy. Show clearly why it is not possible to give a more exact answer.

1 For each of these rectangles, find the limits of accuracy of the area. The accuracy of each measurement is given.

    a   3 cm × 8 cm   (nearest cm)   **b**   3.2 cm × 6.4 cm   (1 dp)

    c   7.86 cm × 18.78 cm   (2 dp)

2 A rectangular garden has sides of 8 m and 5 m, measured to the nearest centimetre.

    a   Write down the limits of accuracy for each length.

    b   What is the maximum area of the garden?

    c   What is the minimum perimeter of the garden?

3 A playground is measured as 32 m by 45 m, to the nearest metre. Calculate the limits of accuracy for the area of the playground.

4 The measurements, to the nearest centimetre, of a box are given as 12 cm × 8 cm × 5 cm. Calculate the limits of accuracy for the volume of the box.

5 The area of a field is given as 400 m^2, to the nearest 10 m^2. One length is given as 24 m, to the nearest metre. Find the limits of accuracy for the other length of the field.

6 In triangle ABC, AB = 8 cm, BC = 6 cm, and ∠ABC = 42°. All the measurements are given to the nearest unit.

    a   Calculate the limits of accuracy for the area of the triangle.

    b   Calculate the smallest possible length of AC.

7 A stop-watch records the time for the winner of a 100-metre race as 12.3 seconds, measured to the nearest one-tenth of a second.

    a   What are the greatest and least possible times for the winner?

    b   The length of the 100-metre track is correct to the nearest 1 centimetre. What are the greatest and least possible lengths of the track?

    c   What is the fastest possible average speed of the winner?

8 A cube has a volume of 27 cm^3, to the nearest cm^3. Find the range of possible values of the side length of the cube.

9 A cube has a volume of 125 cm^3, to the nearest 1 cm^3. Find the limits of accuracy of the area of one side of the square base.

⭐**10** In the triangle ABC, the length of side AB is 42 cm to the nearest centimetre. The length of side AC is 35 cm to the nearest centimetre. The angle C is 61° to the nearest degree. What is the largest possible size that angle B could be?

Not to scale

24   Inequalities and regions

1 Solve the following linear inequalities.

    a $x + 3 < 8$ **b** $t - 2 > 6$ **c** $p + 3 \geqslant 11$

    d $4x - 5 < 7$ **e** $3y + 4 \leqslant 22$ **f** $2t - 5 > 13$

g $\dfrac{x+3}{2} < 8$ **h** $\dfrac{y+4}{3} \leqslant 5$ **i** $\dfrac{t-2}{5} \geqslant 7$

j $2(x-3) < 14$ **k** $4(3x+2) \leqslant 32$ **l** $5(4t-1) \geqslant 30$

m $3x+1 \geqslant 2x-5$ **n** $6t-5 \leqslant 4t+3$ **o** $2y-11 \leqslant y-5$

p $3x+2 \geqslant x+3$ **q** $4w-5 \leqslant 2w+2$ **r** $2(5x-1) \leqslant 2x+3$

2 Write down the values of x that satisfies each of the following.

a $x-2 \leqslant 3$, where x is a positive integer.

b $x+3 < 5$, where x is a positive, even integer.

c $2x-14 < 38$, where x is a square number.

d $4x-6 \leqslant 15$, where x is a positive, odd number.

e $2x+3 < 25$, where x is a positive, prime number.

3 Solve the following linear inequalities.

a $9 < 4x+1 < 13$ **b** $2 < 3x-1 < 11$ **c** $-3 < 4x+5 \leqslant 21$

d $2 \leqslant 3x-4 < 15$ **e** $10 \leqslant 2x+3 < 18$ **f** $-5 \leqslant 4x-7 \leqslant 8$

g $3 \leqslant 5x-7 \leqslant 13$ **h** $8 \leqslant 2x+3 < 19$ **i** $7 \leqslant 5x+3 < 24$

HOMEWORK 24B

1 Write down the inequality that is represented by each diagram below.

2 Draw diagrams to illustrate the following.

a $x \leqslant 2$ **b** $x > -3$ **c** $x \geqslant 0$ **d** $x < 4$

e $x \geqslant -3$ **f** $1 < x \leqslant 4$ **g** $-2 \leqslant x \leqslant 4$ **h** $-2 < x < 3$

3 Solve the following inequalities and illustrate their solutions on number lines.

a $x+5 \geqslant 9$ **b** $x+4 < 2$ **c** $x-2 \leqslant 3$ **d** $x-5 > -2$

e $4x+3 \leqslant 9$ **f** $5x-4 \geqslant 16$ **g** $2x-1 > 13$ **h** $3x+6 < 3$

i $3(2x+1) < 15$ **j** $\dfrac{x+1}{2} \leqslant 2$ **k** $\dfrac{x-3}{3}x > 7$ **l** $\dfrac{x+6}{4} \geqslant 1$

4 Solve the following inequalities and illustrate their solutions on number lines.

a $\dfrac{5x+2}{2} > 3$ **b** $\dfrac{3x-4}{5} \leqslant 1$ **c** $\dfrac{4x+3}{2} \geqslant 11$ **d** $\dfrac{2x-5}{4} < 2$

e $\dfrac{8x+2}{3} \leqslant 2$ **f** $\dfrac{7x+9}{5} > -1$ **g** $\dfrac{x-2}{3} \geqslant -3$ **h** $\dfrac{5x-2}{4} \leqslant -1$

HOMEWORK 24C

Solve the following inequalities, showing their solutions on number lines.

1 $x^2 \leqslant 9$ **2** $x^2 > 36$ **3** $x^2 < 100$ **4** $x^2 \geqslant 4$

5 $x^2 \geqslant 25$ **6** $x^2 - 1 > 15$ **7** $x^2 + 2 \leqslant 11$ **8** $x^2 + 3 > 3$

9 $x^2 + 6 > 7$ **10** $x^2 - 4 \geqslant 21$ **11** $2x^2 - 3 > 5$ **12** $x^2 - 3 < 6$

13 $5x^2 + 3 \leqslant 17$ **14** $2x^2 - 5 < 27$ **15** $3x^2 - 19 \geqslant 56$ **16** $x^2 \geqslant 144$

17 $x^2 < 0.16$ **18** $x^2 \geqslant 1.21$ **19** $x^2 - 5 \leqslant 88$ **20** $x^2 > 0.25$

1 **a** Draw the line $y = 3$ (as a solid line). **b** Shade the region defined by $y \geqslant 3$.

2 **a** Draw the line $x = -1$ (as a dashed line). **b** Shade the region defined by $x < -2$.

3 **a** Draw the line $x = -1$ (as a dashed line).
   b Draw the line $x = 3$ (as a solid line) on the same grid.
   c Shade the region defined by $-1 < x \leqslant 3$.

4 **a** On the same grid, draw the regions defined by the inequalities
   i $-2 \leqslant x \leqslant 2$ **ii** $-1 < y \leqslant 3$
   b Are the following points in the region defined by both inequalities?
   i $(2, 2)$ **ii** $(-2, 2)$ **iii** $(-2, -1)$ **iv** $(-2, 3)$

5 **a** Draw the line $y = 2x + 1$ (as a solid line).
   b Shade the region defined by $y \leqslant 2x + 1$.

6 **a** Draw the line $3x + 4y = 12$ (as a dashed line).
   b Shade the region defined by $3x + 4y > 12$.

7 **a** Draw the line $y = 2x - 1$ (as a solid line).
   b Draw the line $x + y = 5$ (as a solid line) on the same diagram.
   c Shade the diagram so that the region defined by $y \geqslant 2x - 1$ is left unshaded.
   d Shade the diagram so that the region defined by $x + y \leqslant 5$ is left unshaded.
   e Show clearly with an R the region defined by both inequalities.

8 **a** Shade $x \leqslant 2$, $y \geqslant x - 2$ and $x + y \geqslant -2$ on the same grid.
   b Show clearly the region defined by all three inequalities by a letter R.

9 **a** On the same grid, draw the regions defined by the following inequalities. (Shade the diagram so that the overlapping region is left blank.)
   i $y < x + 2$ **ii** $y \geqslant 2x - 2$ **iii** $y \geqslant 0$
   b Are the following points in the region defined by all three inequalities?
   i $(0, 2)$ **ii** $(0, -2)$ **iii** $(2, 2)$ **iv** $(4, 4)$

★**10** **a** On a pair of axes, leave unshaded the region represented by the following inequalities. **i** $x \leqslant 2$ **ii** $y > 1$ **iii** $y \leqslant x + 1$
   b Write down the co-ordinates of all the points whose co-ordinates are integers and lie in the region which satisfy all the inequalities in part **a**.

1 A local shop does A4 and A3 photocopies. A4 copies cost 6p. A3 copies cost 20p. How much will
   a x A4 copies cost **b** y A3 copies cost
   c x A4 and y A3 copies together cost?

2 A school canteen sells pizza at 50p a slice and chips at 75p per bag. How much do each of the following cost?
   a two slices of pizza and a bag of chips. **b** x slices of pizza and y bags of chips.
   c Frank has £5. How much change will he get if he buys x slices of pizza and two bags of chips? Can $x = 8$?

3 Apple computers make two main computers. The G3 and the G4. G3s cost £A and G4s cost £B. How much are
   a x G3s and y G4s **b** x G3s and three times as many G4s
   c x G3s and $(x + 5)$ G4s?

4 If $2x + y < 30$, which of the following may be true?

    a $x + y = 10$ **b** $2x > 30$ **c** $2x + y \leqslant 40$

5 Tins of pears cost 60p. Tins of peaches cost 75p. Mary has £6.00. She buys x tins of pears and y tins of peaches. Explain why $4x + 5y < 40$.

6 Gwen is going on holiday for 14 days. She is taking x paperback novels and y magazines. It takes her three days to read a novel and one day to read a magazine. She gets bored with magazines so needs at least three novels. Because of space in her luggage she cannot take more than seven books and magazines altogether.

    a Explain why $3x + y \leqslant 14$, $x \geqslant 3$, $x + y \leqslant 7$

    b Which of these combinations satisfies all the above requirements

        i   3 books and 4 magazines   **ii**   4 books and 3 magazines

        iii 4 books and 4 magazines   **iv** 2 books and 5 magazines?

★7 The school hall seats a maximum audience of 200 people for performances. Tickets for the school concert cost £2 or £3 each. The school needs to raise at least £450 from this concert. It is decided that the number of £3 tickets must not be greater than twice the number of £2 tickets. There are x tickets at £2 each and y tickets at £3 each.

    Explain why   **i** $x + y \leqslant 200$ **ii** $2x + 3y \geqslant 450$ **iii** $y \leqslant 2x$

8 Computer Zip disks come in two sizes, 100 Mb and 250 Mb. 100 Mb disks cost £6 and 250 Mb cost £25 each. The company buys x 100 Mb disks and y 250 Mb disks. A company has a budget of £300 to spend on disks.

    a Explain why $6x + 25y \leqslant 300$

    b The company needs at least 4000 Mb of storage. Explain why $2x + 5y \geqslant 80$

    c Which of these combinations of disks will satisfy the requirements

        i $(0, 16)$ **ii** $(2, 15)$ **iii** $(1, 16)$?

9 Fred goes to the shop for some tins of peas and beans. Tins of beans cost 60p. Tins of peas cost 40p. He buys x tins of beans and y tins of peas.

    a Fred has £3 to spend. Explain why $3x + 2y \leqslant 15$

    b Fred's mum told him to make sure he has at least two more tins of peas than beans. Explain why $y - x \geqslant 2$

    c Find a combination of tins that satisfy both requirements.

10 Rachel keeps horses and donkeys. She has x donkeys and y horses.

    a Donkeys cost £12 per week to keep and horses cost £15 per week to keep. Rachel has a weekly budget of £210 to feed her animals. Write down an inequality that satisfies this requirement. Simplify your answer as much as possible.

    b Donkeys need at least 60 m^2 to graze and horses need at least 30 m^2 to graze. Rachel's field has an area of 600 m^2. Write down an inequality that satisfies this requirement.

    c Rachel needs at least 2 horses. Find a combination of donkeys and horses that satisfies all of the above conditions.

11 Steve keeps finches and budgies. He has x budgies and y finches.

    a Budgies cost 50p a week to feed and finches cost 60p a week to feed. Steve has £12 a week to spare for food. Write down and simplify an inequality that satisfies this restriction.

    b Budgies need at least 0.2 cubic metres of space and finches need at least 0.15 cubic metres of space. Steve has a shed that has 4 cubic metres of space. Show that $4x + 3y \leqslant 80$

    c To stop fighting there must be at least twice as many finches as budgies. Write down an inequality that satisfies this restriction.

d Can Steve keep
    i five budgies and 16 finches   **ii** seven budgies and 13 finches
    iii six budgies and 14 finches?

★**12** A company is opening a site for caravans and tents. Each caravan requires 100 m^2 of land and each tent 50 m^2. There is a total of 2000 m^2 of land available. For each caravan rented, the firm makes £10 profit per night and for each tent £8 per night. The local council say that there can be no more than twice as many tents as caravans. x caravan plots and y tent plots are taken.

  a Write down two inequalities which must be true.

  b Find the maximum value of $x + y$, subject to all three conditions.

  c How much profit does the company make?

25   Vectors

HOMEWORK 25A

1 Vectors **a**, **b** and **c** are shown on the diagram.

  a Draw the vectors represented by
    i a + b   **ii** –a   **iii** a – b   **iv** b – a   **v** –b
    vi –a – b

  b Explain the connection between the answers to parts **i** and **vi** and parts **iii** and **iv**

2 The diagram shows vectors **a**, **b** and **c**.

  a Draw the vectors shown by   **i** a + b   **ii** a + b + c

  b Explain the answer to **a** part **ii**

  c Write the vectors **a**, **b** and **c** as column vectors and then write as column vectors
    i a – b   **ii** a – c   **iii** a + b + c

3 The diagram shows three vectors **a**, **b** and **c**.
  a is $\vec{OA}$, **b** is $\vec{OB}$ and **c** is $\vec{OC}$.
  a is the vector $\binom{2}{2}$,   **b** is the vector $\binom{4}{1}$
  c is the vector $\binom{6}{0}$

  a Write as a column vector and show on a diagram the vectors
    i $\vec{AB}$ **ii** $\vec{AC}$ **iii** $\vec{BC}$

  b What do your answers to **a** tell you?

  c Would parts **i** and **ii** of **a** be enough to tell you that ABC is a straight line? Explain your answer.

4 $\vec{OA}$ and $\vec{OB}$ are vectors **a** and **b**. M is the midpoint of AB.

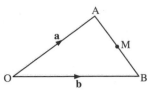

  a Express in terms of **a** and **b** the vectors

  i $\vec{AB}$ **ii** $\vec{AM}$ **iii** $\vec{OM}$

  b Draw on a copy of the diagram the points X and Y such

  that $\vec{OX} = 2\mathbf{a} + \mathbf{b}$ and $\vec{OY} = \mathbf{a} + 2\mathbf{b}$

  Express $\vec{XY}$ in terms of **a** and **b**.

  c What other vector on the diagram is equivalent to $\vec{XY}$?

5 OACB is a trapezium, where $\vec{OA} = \mathbf{a}$, $\vec{OB} = \mathbf{b}$ and $\vec{BC} = 2\mathbf{a}$. P and Q are the mid-points of $\vec{OB}$ and $\vec{AC}$. Express in terms of **a** and **b**.

  a $\vec{OP}$ **b** $\vec{AQ}$ **c** $\vec{PQ}$ **d** How can you tell that $\vec{PQ}$ is parallel to $\vec{OA}$?

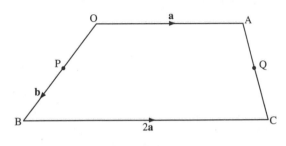

6 $\vec{OA}$, $\vec{OB}$ are the vectors **a** and **b**. C is the point on AB such that C is $\frac{3}{4}$ along AB.

  a Express $\vec{OC}$ in terms of **a** and **b**.

  b If D is the point that is $\frac{2}{3}$ along AC, write down the vector $\vec{OD}$.

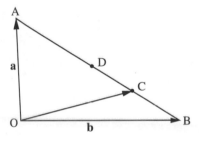

★7 In the diagram, X is the point on AB such that AX = 4XB. Given that $\vec{OA} = 10\mathbf{q}$ and $\vec{OB} = 5\mathbf{p}$, express in terms of **p** and/or **q**,

  a $\vec{AB}$ **b** $\vec{AX}$ **c** $\vec{OX}$

Not to scale

HOMEWORK 25B ✕

1 OACB is a rectangle. $\vec{OA} = \mathbf{a}$ and $\vec{OB} = \mathbf{b}$.

Q is the mid-point of BC and P divides BA in the ratio 1 : 2. Find the vectors

  a $\vec{BP}$ **b** $\vec{OP}$ **c** $\vec{OQ}$

  d Explain the relationship between O, P and Q.

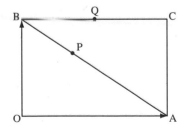

2 $\vec{OA} = \mathbf{a}$. $\vec{OB} = \mathbf{b}$. P is the point that divides OB in the ratio 1 : 2. Q is the point that divides OA in the ratio 2 : 1.

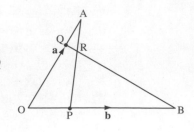

    a Express in terms of $\mathbf{a}$ and $\mathbf{b}$ **i** $\vec{AP}$ **ii** $\vec{BQ}$

    b Explain why OR can be written as $\mathbf{a} + n\vec{AP}$.

    c Explain why OR can be written as $\mathbf{b} + m\vec{BQ}$.

    d Show that the expressions in parts **b** and **c** are equal when $n = \frac{3}{7}$ and $m = \frac{6}{7}$.

    e Hence find the vector $\vec{OR}$ in terms of $\mathbf{a}$ and $\mathbf{b}$.

3 OAB is a triangle. $\vec{OA} = \mathbf{a}$. $\vec{OB} = \mathbf{b}$. R is the mid-point of AB. Q is the mid-point of OA. Find in terms of $\mathbf{a}$ and $\mathbf{b}$ the vectors

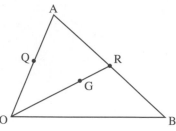

    a $\vec{OR}$ **b** $\vec{QB}$

    c G is the point where OR and QB meet. Explain why $\vec{OG}$ can be written both as $n\vec{OR}$ and $\frac{1}{2}\mathbf{a} + m(\vec{QB})$.

    d You are given that $m + n = 1$.
        Find values of m and n that satisfy the equations in **c**.

    e Hence express $\vec{OG}$ in terms of $\mathbf{a}$ and $\mathbf{b}$.

4 OAB is a triangle. P, Q and R are the mid-points of OB, OA and AB. $\vec{OR} = \mathbf{a}$ and $\vec{OP} = \mathbf{b}$.

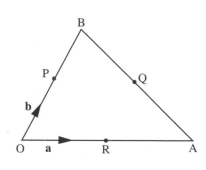

    a Express in terms of $\mathbf{a}$ and $\mathbf{b}$ the vectors
        i $\vec{RP}$ **ii** $\vec{AB}$

    b What do your answers to part **a** tell you about the relationship between the lines RP and AB?

5 OAC is a triangle such that $\vec{OC} = 12\mathbf{q}$, $OB = 3\mathbf{q}$ and $\vec{OA} = 3\mathbf{p}$.

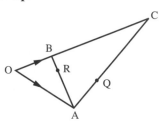

    a Find in terms of $\mathbf{p}$ and $\mathbf{q}$ the vectors
        i $\vec{AB}$ **ii** $\vec{AC}$

    b Given that $AQ = \frac{1}{3}AC$ express $\vec{OQ}$ in terms of $\mathbf{p}$ and $\mathbf{q}$.

    c Given that $\vec{OR} = \mathbf{p} + 2\mathbf{q}$ what can you say about the points O, R and Q?

6 OABC is a quadrilateral. $\vec{OA} = \mathbf{a}$, $\vec{OB} = \mathbf{b}$, $\vec{OC} = \mathbf{c}$. M, N, Q and P are the mid-points of OA, OB, CB and OC.

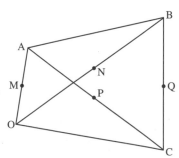

    a Find in terms of $\mathbf{a}$, $\mathbf{b}$ and $\mathbf{c}$ the vectors
        i $\vec{BC}$ **ii** $\vec{NQ}$ **iii** $\vec{MP}$

    b What type of quadrilateral is MNQP? Explain your answer.

★7 OACB and OBRS are parallelograms.
$\vec{OA}$ is **a**, $\vec{OB}$ is **b**, and $\vec{BR}$ is **r**. Find in terms of **a**, **b**, and **r** expressions in their simplest forms for

a $\vec{OR}$

b $\vec{SB}$

c $\vec{OX}$, where X is the mid-point of AR,
i.e. $\frac{1}{2}(\vec{AO} + \vec{OR})$

26 Transformation of graphs

HOMEWORK 26A

Do not use a graphical calculator.

1 On the same axes sketch the graphs of
  a $y = x^2$ **b** $y = 2x^2$ **c** $y = x^2 + 2$ **d** $y = (x + 2)^2$
  e Describe the transformation(s) that take(s) the graph in part **a** to each of the graphs in parts **b** to **d**.

2 On the same axes sketch the graphs of
  a $y = x^2$ **b** $y = 3x^2 + 2$ **c** $y = x^2 - 3$ **d** $y = \frac{1}{2}x^2 + 1$
  e Describe the transformation(s) that take(s) the graph in part **a** to each of the graphs in parts **b** to **d**.

3 On the same axes sketch the graphs of
  a $y = x^2$ **b** $y = (x + 4)^2$ **c** $y = -x^2$ **d** $y = 2 - x^2$
  e Describe the transformation(s) that take(s) the graph in part **a** to each of the graphs in parts **b** to **d**.

4 On the same axes sketch the graphs of
  a $y = \sin x$ **b** $y = 3 \sin x$ **c** $y = \sin x + 3$ **d** $y = \sin (x + 30°)$
  e Describe the transformation(s) that take(s) the graph in part **a** to each of the graphs in parts **b** to **d**.

5 On the same axes sketch the graphs of
  a $y = \sin x$ **b** $y = -\sin x$ **c** $y = \sin \frac{x}{3}$ **d** $y = 3 \sin \frac{x}{2}$
  e Describe the transformation(s) that take(s) the graph in part a to each of the graphs in parts **b** to **d**.

6 On the same axes sketch the graphs of
  a $y = \sin x$ **b** $y = 3 \sin x$ **c** $y = \sin (x + 45°)$ **d** $y = 2 \sin (x + 90°)$
  e Describe the transformation(s) that take(s) the graph in part **a** to the graphs in parts **b** to **d**.

7 On the same axes sketch the graphs of
  a $y = \cos x$ **b** $y = -\cos x$ **c** $y = \cos x + 4$ **d** $y = 2 \cos x$
  e Describe the transformation(s) that take(s) the graph in part **a** to each of the graphs in parts **b** to **d**.

8 On the same axes sketch the graphs of

    a $y = \cos x$ **b** $y = 3 \cos x$ **c** $y = \cos (x + 60°)$ **d** $y = 2 \cos x + 3$

    e Describe the transformation(s) that take(s) the graph in part **a** to each of the graphs in parts **b** to **d**.

9 Explain why the graphs of $y = \cos x$ and $y = \sin (x + 90°)$ are the same.

★**10** The table shows some values of the function $f(x) = (x - 2)^2 + 4$, where $-3 < x < 4$.

    a Draw the graph of $y = f(x)$.

    b On the same axes, draw the graph of $y = x^2$.

x	-3	-2	-1	0	1	2	3	4
$f(x)$	29	20	13	8	5	4	5	8

    c Describe how the graph of $y = (x - 2)^2 + 4$ can be obtained from the graph $y = x^2$ by a transformation. State clearly what this transformation is.

11 The graphs below are all transformations of $y = x^2$. Two points through which each graph passes are indicated. Use this information to work out the equation of each graph.

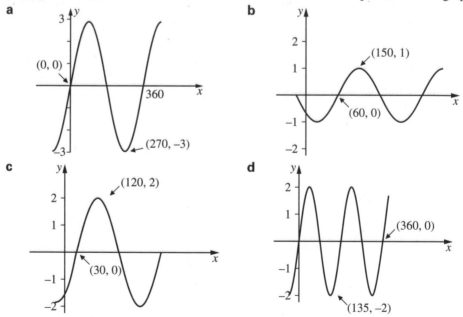

12 The graphs below are all transformations of $y = \sin x$. Two points through which each graph passes are indicated. Use this information to work out the equation of each graph.

13 Below are the graphs of $y = - \sin x$ and $y = \cos x$.

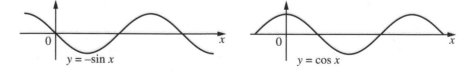

    a Describe a series of transformations that would take the first graph to the second.

    b Which of the following is equivalent to $y = - \sin x$?

      i $y = \sin (x + 180°)$ **ii** $y = \cos (x + 90°)$ **iii** $y = 2 \sin \dfrac{x}{2}$

★14 The graph of $y = f(x)$ has been drawn.
Sketch the graph of
   a $y = f(x) - 2$ **b** $y = f(x - 2)$

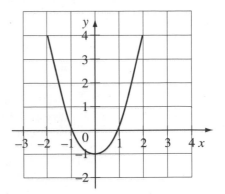

27   Proof use

Only one set of questions is given for this chapter. Questions should be chosen that are appropriate to current work.

1   Hollow squares are surrounded by 1 centimetre cubes.
e.g. this is a 5×5 hollow square.
Prove that when a $m \times m$ hollow square is placed inside a $n \times n$ hollow square the amount of space left is $n^2 - 4(n + m) + 8$.

2   If m and n are integers then $(m^2 - n^2)$, $2mn$ and $(m^2 + n^2)$ will form three sides of a right angled triangle. e.g. Let $m = 5$ and $n = 3$, $m^2 - n^2 = 16$, $2mn = 30$, $m^2 + n^2 = 34$ and $34^2 = 1156$, $16^2 + 30^2 = 256 + 900 = 1156$
Prove this result.

3   Explain why the triangle number sequence 1, 3, 6, 10, 15, 21, 28, ...
follows the pattern of two odd numbers followed by two even numbers.

4   $10p + q$ is a multiple of 7. Prove that $3p + q$ is also a multiple of 7.

5   ABCD is a trapezium. The diagonals DB and AC meet at E.
Prove that the triangles ADE and BCE are equal in area.

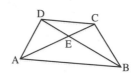

6   **a**   Show that $2(5(x - 2) + y) = 10(x - 1) + 2y - 10$.
    b   Prove that this trick works:
           Think of two numbers less than 10.
           Subtract 2 from the larger number and then multiply by 5.
           Add the smaller number and multiply by 2.
           Add 9 and subtract the smaller number.
           Add 1 to both the tens digits and the units digits to obtain the numbers first thought of.

c Prove why the following trick works.

    Choose two numbers. One with one digit the other with 2 digits.

    Subtract 9 times the first number from 10 times the second number.

    The units digit of the answer is the single digit number chosen and the sum of the other digits plus the units digit is the other number chosen.

    e.g. Choose 7 and 23. $(23 \times 10) - (7 \times 9) = 167$.

    The single digit number chosen is 7 the two digits number chosen is $16 + 7 = 23$.

7 ABCD is a rectangle. CEF is a triangle congruent to triangle ACD. BCE is a straight line. The line AC is extended to meet EF at P. Prove that AP is perpendicular to EF.

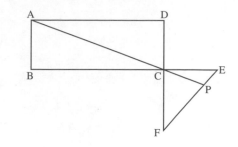

8 Prove that $(3n - 1)^2 + (3n)^2 + (3n + 1)^2 = (5n)^2 + (n - 1)^2 + (n + 1)^2$.

9 Prove that $(n - 1)^2 + n^2 + (n + 1)^2 = 3n^2 + 2$.

10 **a** What is the mth term of the sequence 4, 9, 14, 19, 24, … ?

    b What is the mth term of the sequence 5, 10, 15, 20, 25, … ?

    c If T_n represent the nth triangle number prove that $T_n = \frac{1}{2}n(n+1)$

    d Prove that T_n is a multiple of 5 when n is a member of the series

        4, 5, 14, 15, 19, 20, 24, 25, …

11 If T_n is any triangle number prove that

    $3T_n = T_{2n+1} - T_{n+1}$ e.g. $T_4 = 10$, $T_9 = 45$, $T_5 = 15$; $3 \times 10 = 45 - 15$

12 An isosceles trapezium is cut along a diagonal and the pieces put together as shown.

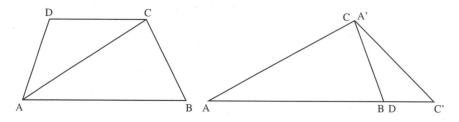

    a Prove that ABC is a straight line.   **b** Prove that the triangle is isosceles.

    c Explain why the triangle formed could never be equilateral.

13 If T_n is any triangle number prove that $\dfrac{T_n - 1}{(T_n)} = \dfrac{(n - 1)(n + 2)}{n(n + 1)}$

14 **a** What is the nth term of the sequence 1, 4, 7, 10, 13, 16, … .

    b Explain why there is no multiple of 3 in the sequence.

    c Prove that the sum of any 5 consecutive numbers in the sequence is a multiple of 5.

15 This question was first set in an examination in 1929.

    $10^x = \dfrac{a}{b}$, $10^y = \dfrac{b}{a}$, Prove that $x + y = 0$

16 **a** Prove the alternate segment theorem.

   b Two circles touch internally at T. The common
   tangent at T is drawn. Two lines TAB and TXY are
   drawn from T. Prove that AX is parallel to BY.

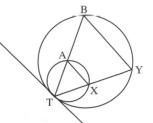

17 Two circles touch externally at T. A line ATB
   is drawn through T. The common tangent at T and
   the tangents at A and B meet at P and Q. prove that
   PB is parallel to AQ.

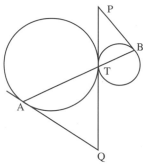

18 *m* and *n* are integers. Explain why

   a the product $n(n + 1)$ must be even   **b** $2m + 1$ is always an odd number.

   c Look at the following numbers pattern

   $$1^2 - 1 = \mathbf{0}$$
   $$2^2 - 1 = 3$$
   $$3^2 - 1 = \mathbf{8}$$
   $$4^2 - 1 = 15$$
   $$5^2 - 1 = \mathbf{24}$$
   $$6^2 - 1 = 35$$

   i Extend the pattern for five more lines to show that alternate values are multiples of 8.

   ii Prove that this is true.

19 The midpoints of the edges of a square are
   joined to a vertex to create a smaller square (shown
   shaded). Explain why the shaded square has an area
   one-fifth of the area of the larger square.

20 ABC is a triangle. P is a point on BC such
   that angle APC = angle BAC. The sides of ABC
   are *a*, *b* and *c*. AP = *p* and PC = *r*.

   Prove that $r = \dfrac{b^2}{a}$.

   (Hint: Show that triangles ABC and APC are
   similar).

21 *a*, *b*, *c* and *d* are four consecutive integers. Prove that

   a $bc - ad = 2$ **b** $ab + bc + cd + da + 1$ is a square number.

22 Prove that the square of the sum of two consecutive integers minus the sum of the squares
   of the two integers is four times a triangular number.

   e.g. Let the two integers be 6 and 7. $(6 + 7)^2 - (6^2 + 7^2) = 169 - 85 = 84 = 4 \times 21$

23 a, b, c, d are consecutive integers. Prove that $bd - ac$ is always odd.

24 **a** Prove that the angles subtended by the chord at the circumference of a circle are equal.

   b PQRS is a cyclic quadrilateral. PR and QS meet at T. Angles x, $2x$, $3x$ and $5x$ are marked on the diagram.

   i Find x.

   ii Show that the angles of the quadrilateral and angle STP form a number sequence.

25 p, q and r are three consecutive numbers. Prove that $pr = q^2 - 1$.

26 ACB and ADB are right angled triangles. The lengths are as marked.

   a Use Pythagoras' theorem to show that $x^2 = r^2 + s^2$

   b Use Pythagoras' theorem on both triangles ACB and ADB to prove that $xt = sy$.

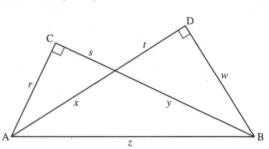